MW00563504

NOT VERY
INTELLIGENT
DESIGN

NOT VERY INTELLIGENT DESIGN

On the origin, creation and evolution of
the theory of intelligent design

by
Neel Ingman
and
Mark Ingman

ABOUT THE AUTHORS

Mark Ingman is the less famous brother of reclusive blogger, Neel Ingman, who is almost entirely unknown for publishing his conversations with God, the Pope, and other things at neelingman.com.

Mark Ingman has never seen or experienced anything without feeling the need to criticize, rate and redesign it. When he walks into a house he'll almost always notice that the bathroom is in the wrong place, and that the alignment of the structure totally ignores the path of the sun.

Neel Ingman is less opinionated, but is still prepared to discuss and, if necessary, debate any topic at any time, with anybody or anything.

Sturgeon's Law says that 90% of everything is crap. Mark Ingman thinks at least 99% of everything is crap.

Most conversations with Mark and Neel involve something getting a mark out of ten and may contain up to 90% digression and hearsay.

Version 1.1

First Publication, 2018

Palaceno House
Auckland
New Zealand

ISBN 978-0-473-43342-0 (Softcover)
ISBN 978-0-473-43343-7 (Epub)
ISBN 978-0-473-43344-4 (Kindle)
ISBN 978-0-473-43345-1 (PDF)
ISBN 978-0-473-43346-8 (iBook)

neelingman.com

NotVeryIntelligentDesign.com

kneelingman.com

Available from Amazon.com

To be notified about new books by this author,

sign up to the mailing list at

neelingman.com

CONTENTS

INTRODUCTION

The imagination of the human mind is a wonderful thing. Arguably the most wonderful thing about us. Without imagination, invention is impossible. If you can't imagine that an axe may be useful, you've no chance of inventing one.

But there are limits to our imagination, and they seem to have a lot to do with our physicality. We can easily form a clear mental picture of the chunk of time it takes for the blink of an eye, a football match, or a few lifetimes. Much beyond that it gets a lot harder. A ten thousandth of a second is fifty times longer than a five hundred thousandth of a second, but, in our minds they may as well be identical.

Likewise with a long time. A clear understanding of a few thousand years is hazy at best, and millions of years is downright impossible. A million years and a million million years are effectively identical to all humans, except for some scientists, but they also claim to understand nine dimensional space so who knows what the hell's going on in those brains.

The inability to grasp extremes of time is connected to the phenomenon of time appearing to accelerate as we get older. Everybody agrees that it happens, but not many seem to have given very much thought as to why it happens. Our personal mental clocks began ticking the moment we were born (or some time after that, nobody remembers the early months), so that's when time began for us. And that's why a year is a very long time for a five-year old (less than a fifth of all known time from the very beginning) and goes by very quickly for a fifty-year old (a mere 2 percent of a lifetime so far).

Our comprehension of time is linked to, and limited by, our intrinsic personal clock.

Similarly, our comprehension of size and distance is limited by our physical size and mobility. By the time you can fit millions of something on the head of a pin, it's impossible to imagine what one of them, say a proton, might look like in the palm of your hand. Then think about an electron, which is 2000 times smaller. No mental picture available. They may as well be identical.

A few hundred years ago, being about as much time as we can get a reasonable grasp of, most people didn't travel much beyond the thicket over the hill behind the stream. They would have had great difficulty comprehending how far it was to walk five hundred miles, let alone to walk five hundred more, because back then nobody had walked a thousand miles just to be the man to fall down at her door.

These days we can easily comprehend distances such as the circumference of the earth, because we travel that far, but even the moon would have most people struggling to get an accurate handle on how many days it would take to walk there, were that possible. (It would take about nine years non-stop, at a brisk clip. If you kept going it would take 168,754 years to get to Pluto. Longer if you were to stop for lunch or a nap.)

The point of all of which is to say that none of us has any grasp of how long ago time began, or how far it is to the edge of the universe, because these things are way beyond the limits of human imagination, let alone actual comprehension.

Which doesn't seem to bother the two groups of people who claim to know quite a lot about the beginning of time. Scientists and theologians. And of course they don't agree. To prevail in that debate would require being able to define the beginning of everything, including the beginning of time. Arguments are made using unfathomably complicated mathematical equations on one side and old books on the other. Even with those aids, it's still incomprehensible to normal people, as the scientific explanation ceases to apply just short of the goal line, and, on the other side everything apparently requires a creator, except for the creator. Something either came from nothing, before which not even time existed, or there was always something there. Neither side gets anywhere near providing a basic, easily explained, verifiable understanding of the concept of where we came from or how we got here.

So we're going to leave aside the debate between evolution and creationism. Instead we'll just take a good close look at the evidence that's actually in front of us. The human body as it currently exists.

Works of this nature generally begin with one or more initial assumptions. For the sake of argument, which is really the point of this whole exercise, and because we enjoy a good argument, we'll assume the position that the human animal was designed by an intelligent designer.

From that assumption we'll analyze and judge the design of each part of the human body, out of ten, in terms of excellence or even plain competence, given the tools of the designer. (The designer's tools may or may not have been governed by what we currently understand to be the laws of biology, chemistry, physics etc, as the designer may well have designed those too.)

To illustrate the marking system, here are a couple of examples.

The original Chevrolet Corvair was such a piece of crap that only Corvair enthusiasts or collectors could give it more than half a point. A new S-class Mercedes is at least an eight, regardless of any personal prejudice.

The first aircraft that flew was a magnificent achievement but next to a Dreamliner it's barely a one compared to the 787's eight or nine. And it only gets the one as a nod to the era in which it was created. If someone designed a plane like that today, it would get zero. At the time of its invention, it was an easy ten. And the Dreamliner will probably be more like a four or five in fifty years' time. Or less, if the engines keep blowing up.

The designer of man, however, doesn't qualify for any era-related consolation points for things that may not have been understood back in the day, as he's also credited with designing the whole universe, so he must have already understood everything there is to know about everything.

It's been said that any task is achievable if you tackle it piece by piece. So this book will analyze and rate the design of the human being, piece by piece, and will complete the exercise by considering the overall design as a whole.

So where to begin? It's usually wise, when doing tasks around the house that may involve spillage or other messiness, to start at the top and work down from there. So that's what we'll do.

HAIR

People spend a lot of time and money on hair. Washing, cutting, styling, straightening, curling and coloring. Some even go for replanting. Or plucking. In days gone by, a noble hairline (these days known as a fivehead, being approximately 25% larger than a forehead) was achieved by women having the front of their scalp plucked bare.

The plucked forehead phenomenon originated after the Queen of Belgium's fourth cousin, Philomena Pluck, was mercilessly mocked as a young woman by other junior members of the royal court on account of her massive forehead. Pluck endured the taunting for some months before formulating a plan to rise to the throne and thereby ensure that her appearance became the desirable norm. By systematically poisoning, throat slitting and eye gouging her fellow courtiers, fifteen in all, Philomena cleared the way to be the unchallenged heiress to the throne. A royal stenographer was reported to have idly jested "hairless heiress" shortly before his disappearance. This was thought to have had something to do with the Queen's fatal fall from her bedroom window the following day, making Philomena an heiress no longer.

Queen Philomena decreed that any woman with an ignoble hairline would not be received at court or be eligible for marriage to any nobleman. Thus the noble hairline became immediately fashionable and, perhaps surprisingly, remained de rigueur for more than seventy years following Philomena's untimely death.

What's the point of having hair on the scalp? Hair that keeps on growing and needs cutting annoyingly often. Long hair gets in the way. And the longer it is, the more of a nuisance it is. Long hair can end up in your soup, in your mouth, in your eyes on a windy day, or between the sticky fingers of the pervert sitting behind you on the bus.

Scalp hair affects our self perception. Usually adversely. How's my hair looking today? Not greasy I hope. I wonder if it needs a cut? What's fashionable right now for someone like me? What is someone like me? What should I try to look like? I don't want to look like an idiot or a nerd. Or are nerds cool now? Is cool still a cool word to use? I don't know. And I don't want to look like I'm trying too hard. Or have a style that's age inappropriate. Will the mullet come back? Was it ever cool?

It's hard to feel good when you think your hair looks bad. Men go to great lengths to pretend they're not bald. Tattooed stubble. The hair piece or full rug. The jaunty hat. The punch 'n' grow. The comb-over. The spray thickener. Even the double reverse comb-over with orange spray thickener and lashings of glue, which could only possibly look sensible in the mirror of a narcissist with a massive self-perception problem.

Cats never need a haircut and never have a bad hair day. They have hair that grows to a sensible length, long enough to provide coverage and protection from the sun, and then it stops. Which would have been a great solution for the scalp of man, and entirely possible given that cats were designed at pretty much the same time as man. So hair that never stops growing must have been a conscious design decision. A really bad one.

Short hair still has the potential to host nits and head lice and other mini-nasties, so while it would have been an improvement on never-stop-growing hair, it's still not perfect.

Hair anywhere on the head seems to be entirely unnecessary. Sufferers of alopecia totalis are only sufferers because they don't look the same as everybody else and may feel a little self-conscious as a result. Black guys look good with shaved heads. Middle-aged, chubby white guys don't. But if nobody had any hair on their head, we'd all be happy that we're having the equivalent of a good hair day, every day. And none of us would have to give even a moment's thought to hair maintenance. Win win. Although we might sometimes need a hat on sunny days. Unless our skin and eyes were better designed. We'll get to that.

Human scalp hair - 2/10 (Only because it's a job creator.)

Facial hair. What the hell's the point? Women and children do perfectly well without it and don't have to spend any time on maintenance. If a man leaves his face untrimmed, every pie becomes a hair pie. For fellow diners, the sight of a heavily mustached man sifting his soup through the weir on his upper lip is not pleasant. And, once again, why does it need to keep growing? Cats have facial hair, but around the mouth it's only about a millimeter long. Without ever needing to be trimmed.

Short-haired cat hair - 8/10 (Because it's really sensible.)

Most men are forced into a daily regime of shaving in order to avoid itchy stubble. And it's well known that women don't enjoy stubble rash either on the face, or on the inner thigh, no matter how little they may complain at the time of acquisition.

Would anyone opt for facial hair if it didn't carry any social significance? If facial hair didn't exist there'd be no need to signal your fondness for hipsterism, suicide bombing or any other absurdity by growing a huge unruly bush on your mush.

Facial hair - 0/10 (Contender for stupidest design award.)

A cat on your head doesn't feel anywhere near as cuddly as a cat on the bare skin of your face, (provided you've had a shave), and the bare skin on skin sensation of touching someone you really fancy should be enough evidence to prove that all hair is really just a nuisance. Which is something porn stars discovered first. We'll get to that soon.

Hair - 1/10

EYES

Eyes are the windows to the soul. Eyes can pierce, bewitch, beguile, tell, or hide. They can be sleepy, bloodshot, tired, shifty, beady, bedroom or dead. We see deep meaning in each other's eyes. Love at first sight requires eye contact.

With the possible exception of the booty in recent years, eyes are the most popular body part for writing songs about. Bette Davis' Eyes, Crying Eyes, Lyin' Eyes, Smoke Gets in Your Eyes, even Eyes Without a Face. A splash of Clorox is the only thing likely to Make My Brown Eye Blue but that's got nothing to do with A Pair of Brown Eyes, a Brown Eyed Girl or what happens Behind Blue Eyes.

Such an amount of praise and attention would seem to indicate that eyes are an exquisite piece of design. But there are a few negatives.

The human eye generally begins to fail when the human animal's about half way through its life. If the power steering in your car failed at 50,000km, you'd accept it as bad luck and pay to have it repaired. But if you found out that every single car of that type had power steering failure at a similar mileage, you'd be upset and angry at the incompetence of the manufacturer. If you couldn't afford to have the power steering unit replaced, you may decide to attach a steering wheel knob to help you apply sufficient muscle power to make tight turns, like bus and taxi drivers used to have in days gone by.

When your eyes begin to fail you need the equivalent of that steering wheel knob. Meaning reading glasses. Most people over the age of forty learn what a total pain in the arse it is to need these things. Sooner or later you need two or three different steering wheel knobs for different situations, but you can't have them all attached to your face at once. So you find yourself trying to back into a tight parking space with no way of seeing what you're doing. Which is massively annoying.

But that's not where the problems begin. If you're born lucky, you'll have 20/20 vision. A lot of people aren't born lucky. There are serious quality control issues.

Everything designed for production has tolerances as part of the design. The first tolerance is to do with physical properties. For example, to be considered "ok", a 10 cm widget must be within .05cm of the designed length, that is between 10.05cm and 9.95cm. All widgets that fall within this range are deemed "ok". Those that don't are discarded. The second tolerance is the percentage of "ok" widgets out of the total production. For example, if the machine producing the widgets pumps out 98% of all widgets in the "ok" tolerance range, that may be deemed acceptable. But if the machine pumps out only 88% of widgets inside the tolerance range, the machine will be shut down and the process will be analyzed right back to looking at the design of the widget, as well as the design and manufacture of the machine, in order to figure out where the problem lies. And to fix it.

More than 20% of humans are born with eyesight that doesn't fall into the 20/20 "ok" tolerance range. That'd be unacceptable to almost any quality controller in any factory on the planet.

Some humans are born short sighted, or myopic, some long sighted, or hyperopic. Some have astigmatism. Some are looking all over the place at the same time. These are the most common eye defects. While present at birth, they generally get worse over the first few years of life. Less than 5% of five year olds are seriously myopic, but this percentage increases to 25% by late teens.

Those lucky enough to have 20/20 vision may think that's worth a good grade for the designer (rather than the quality control department), but could, or should our eyes have been designed better?

Pick up a camera or a pair of binoculars with 8x magnification. That's how much better some eagles and hawks can see. They can spot a tiny rodent a mile away, dive at it from 1,000 feet at 100 miles per hour, keeping it in perfect focus until wham, they've got that garden fresh, free range snack clamped tight in their big powerful claws. So our eye designer's let us down a bit there. (This also inadvertently raises the issue that those creatures can fly. Which is a very much better way of getting around. But that's for later.)

Any cat can see way better than us, especially at night. (Which must be when they eat all the carrots, because they've never been seen eating one during the day.) Insects with compound eyes have pretty much 360-degree vision. Horses maybe 260. Perhaps another pair of eyes on the back of our heads would be useful. Hard to imagine how useful, without ever having had that ability. But driving a car without mirrors, (and no power steering if you're over forty) is considerably trickier than driving with mirrors.

Combine 360-degree vision with night vision as good as owls and there goes all that fear of the dark. That suspicious guy walking up behind you on the sidewalk at night? You could pepper spray him without having to turn your head. And no moron would ever whip your chair away as you were going to sit down. Anything resulting in less opportunity for stupid pranks has to be a bonus.

While cats and sharks can see six and ten times better than humans, respectively, the Leaf Tailed gecko and other nocturnal gecko species can see up to 350 times better than we can in dim light. The ogre-faced spider has six eyes and scientists believe that ogre-faced spiders have better night vision than cats, sharks, or even owls, which can see up to 100 times better than humans at night.

Other creatures can see more of the electromagnetic radiation spectrum than us. We perceive three primary colors but the mantis shrimp sees eleven or twelve. Including ultraviolet and infrared. And they perceive both linear and circular polarization of light. What that would look like, or what benefits it may have, is impossible to imagine. How scientists know that stuff is also impossible to imagine.

On bright sunny days, being the days we really like to go outside, our eyes need protecting from the sun. A redesign to fix that may include a combination of a protruding brow and deeper eye sockets, but mostly lenses that adjust to compensate for brightness. Something which they supposedly do already, but obviously not well enough, or nobody would have bothered inventing sunglasses. Or hats. Often without realizing it, man has been working away at improving on our basic design, or rather designing things to compensate for our basic design flaws, for hundreds of years. Things such as shoes. Which we'll get to later.

To sum up. It's pretty good to be able to see as well as we do, and as long as you're lucky enough to be born with decent eyes (a lot of people aren't, 2 points off for that), our eyes seem okay. We cope just fine. But they could be a lot better. Say the equal of eagles (1 point off), sharks (1 point off), flies (1 point off) and shrimp combined, and they should last as long as the rest of the body (2 points off).

Had the designer taken a look in the parts bin and done a bit of reliability engineering and quality control in the production stage, our eyes could have been way, way better than they are.

Eyes - 3/10   (Very useful when they work.)

NOSES

Noses are an absolute disaster. They run, they bleed, they get blocked, they sneeze, they need blowing and cleaning, and often need picking, usually at traffic lights. And hair grows out the bottom. Bloody hair. Again. (Isn't it about time someone designed a decent nostril hair trimmer?)

Noses stick out like a bowsprit and draw attention to themselves. Our brains have to trick us into pretending our noses are invisible so they don't annoy us by being right there, front and centre, every time we open our eyes.

When some belligerent dickhead decides someone else needs hitting, he'll often go right for the schnoz. Cos it's sitting there like a target. Just asking for it. And a whack on the beak is seriously bloody painful. And bloody. You often have to throw away the shirt you're wearing if you cop one on the nozzle. Or even if you don't. Sometimes noses start bleeding for no obvious reason at all.

Noses are a big factor in determining whether somebody's attractive or ugly. If they're a bit crooked, or in any way asymmetrical, it's game over. Too long or too short. Ugly. Turned up so you can see right into the nostrils, not good. Of all the slang terms for noses - schnozzer, beak, hooter, nozzle, honker, snotlocker, snout - none are complimentary, because a nice nose draws no comment. Only when imperfect, do they warrant describing. A good strong nose is not a compliment. It just means big.

Charles Darwin almost didn't join the crew of HMS Beagle for his famous voyage of discovery after being initially rejected by Captain FitzRoy, who believed the shape of Darwin's nose indicated that he would not possess sufficient energy & determination for the voyage.

Prior to the inspired invention of injecting cement into inadequately-sized buttocks, the nose was far and away the most common site on the human body for a vanity operation. A big hooter without a big ego to support it can become a source of embarrassment for the bearer.

If you're feeling unwell through having caught a cold or similar, liquid snot can stream non-stop for days and won't cease until you've sand-papered all the skin off the end of your beak. Adding indignity to injury. Stupid design. Why doesn't the snot run down the back way instead, straight down your throat, leaving the nostrils clear for breathing. Which is theoretically what they're designed for. This would be the only useful reason to have the multifunction throat design which is otherwise stupid. More on that in the throat section. Why have snot at all?

And what's the point of sneezing? We know what causes it. Allergies, particles touching the bloody nostril hairs, sunlight, temperature change etc. But why? What good does it do to sneeze? Sneezes are great for spreading diseases, but that's hardly a positive design feature. And why do they occur so often whilst eating muesli, arguably the worst and most productive of all sneezes. Muesli does not sit comfortably in either nostril. Delete sneezing from the repertoire along with snot production. A simple upgrade.

From a creator's perspective, noses would be easy to improve. If they had the sole function of breathing, were not subject to ailment related blockages or streaming and were not connected to the eating hole or tubes, they'd be very much better.

Noses - 1/10

EARS

Ears are possibly the most decorative elements of the human body. Most other parts are primarily functional, but the ears are like paisley-shaped, meat doilies attached to the side of the head. Some may suggest that the intricate shape is primarily functional, a set of tuning surfaces designed to focus sounds into the middle ear, but in fact the outer ear can cope with all manner of modification without affecting one's hearing.

Women have been hanging sparkly baubles from their lobes since the day "pretty" became a concept, even punching holes in them for the purpose. More recently people have been stretching the holes more and more with all manner of plugs and inserts, and no longer limit the piercing to the lower lobe, but install multiple metal objects all over the poor, abused flaps of gristle. Reportedly they can still hear perfectly well, it's just their ability to make sense of what they hear that may be a problem.

Sometimes ears stick out too much. This can be remedied by a simple surgical procedure, or ten years playing rugby in the

NOT VERY INTELLIGENT DESIGN

forwards. Which isn't really a remedy, more like a modification. From lettuce leaves blowing in the breeze to cauliflower ears, a symbol of pride for old rugby players and a good way for others to recognize old men who used to stick their heads between other men's bums for recreational pleasure.

Ears are also known for failing earlier than other body parts, but they're not guaranteed to, like eyes. So that's good.

A human ear in good condition can hear sounds from 20Hz to 20kHz, which is the complete audible range. Which sounds like perfect design were it not for the fact that the audible range is defined by the limits of the human ear. Infrasound (below 20Hz) and ultrasound (above 20kHz) would also be parts of the audible range if our ears were less limited.

There are a few things wrong with the design of the human ear.

Earache in babies and children is well known. A better design here would save the little ones the agony of earache, and the rest of us the agony of listening to them screaming. Points off.

Ear wax can be a damned nuisance. At its worst it can cause intense pain when the tray tables are folded and the seat backs are returned to their upright positions. More points off.

Tinnitus. Very common. Like crickets. And very annoying. Also like crickets. At least the noisiest ones. Or the one that gets inside your bedroom that you can't find. It chirps in the dark, and with the light on, stops chirping when you get close, then starts chirping again 23 seconds after you get back into bed and turn the light off. The point of ears is to hear noises. Ears that think they hear noises when there are no noises are not as bad as ears that hear no noises when there are noises, but tinnitus is still a terrible design fault.

Vertigo. As well as hearing, our ears have something to do with our sense of balance. When working properly our balancing system works well enough for us to ride bikes and, for some, to walk across canyons on a strand of wire. The fact that most of us could or would not do this has more to do with the limitations of our brains than our ears. A better design would be for the balance control centre to be independent of the ears so as to avoid one problem causing multiple issues. It might also be better not to have an irrational, sphincter puckering fear of heights. Birds aren't scared to sit on the edge of tall buildings, so why are most of us?

Some animals have better hearing than us on account of being able to move their ears towards sounds to hear them more clearly. Not all animals can move their ears. Not all humans can either. Some can but it's just a silly little, barely visible wiggle for no conceivable reason caused by erratic thoughtless design and/or production irregularities.

Plenty of creatures have better hearing than us. A few examples. The household moggy, as well as having better eyes than us, has way better hearing at the top end. Up to 64 kHz.

The greater wax moth can detect frequencies up to 300kHz, about 15 times higher than humans can hear. And better hearing than bats. Which means they can hear bats' sonar signals and fly away. Or keep still. Or whatever they think's the best defense against a sonar equipped, flying death machine in a pitch black cave.

Some blind humans have managed to develop a basic sonar system like bats. Sonar should have been fitted to all of us as original equipment. Humans are supposed to be the top of the range creature. We should have all the good stuff fitted as standard.

Ears - 5/10   (Includes points for decorative value.)

FACES

Why bother having faces as a separate section when all the individual components are already covered? Because the face you were born with has a massive impact on your whole life. Not just for beauty queens and movie stars. For everybody. It might have been Jim Jefferies who pointed out that the most important thing you can do to ensure you have a happy and successful life is to be good looking. Sad, but true. Unless you're good looking. In which case it's excellent.

Some socially aware liberal thinkers spend a lot of time complaining that TV, movies and advertisements should feature more average looking people in order to more accurately reflect what society is really like. Which is a decent thought and difficult to argue against on a philosophical basis. But in fact casting attractive people is a very accurate reflection of society. Not of what society looks like, but of what society likes to look at. Unless your brain has been trained or washed to think differently, people like looking at attractive people. Both on screen and in real life. Even with their clothes on.

Attractive people get treated better every day. They get better tables in restaurants, better service in shops, and are far more likely to get upgrades on flights. And really attractive people get paid a huge amount of money for doing nothing at all except letting people take photographs of them. Quite often with their clothes off.

Faces fail the quality control test. There are nowhere near enough good looking ones. There is no good reason for any human to be less attractive than a 7. A designer who's happy to churn out so many 3s and 4s is doing a piss poor job. A good face factory should turn out 80% 7s, 15% 8s, 4% 9s and 1% 10s.

And the same should apply to bodies as a whole. Make every body really attractive, with a few gorgeous, beautiful and spectacular ones thrown in to keep it interesting. Looking at an average person isn't difficult, but listening to an average person is pretty much the opposite of interesting. If we had to listen to as many people as we have to look at, it'd be just as important to raise the overall level of intelligence and especially wit.

Every night in Australia, and probably other places too, thousands of parrots arrive home en masse to turn in for the night. Just like the Waltons, every parrot says good night to every other parrot. Which is extremely noisy, even noisier than crickets, and it's why it takes them such a very long time to settle down and shut up. Then just as they calm down a few stragglers arrive and they all have to say good night to everybody all over again. But that's a digression. The point of mentioning ten thousand parrots en masse is that they all look equally attractive. And they all seem to be perfectly happy about that. Obviously they have no trouble procreating.

As things currently stand, many less attractive humans can only get laid with the aid of dim lighting and wine goggles, so better quality control with respect to beauty may also help reduce alcoholism.

If we ignore surreptitious glances at certain other body parts, the face is the main thing we look at when interacting with each other. By flexing certain muscles, we subconsciously change the shape of our faces to express a wide range of emotions. Which we then spend years trying to control in order to conceal when we're bluffing at poker or, more often, simply lying to each other. Being "off your face" is when you lose control of your facial muscles to the extent that you can't fool anyone into thinking that you might be sober.

Faces - 0 to 10/10 (Which is the problem.)

SKULLS

The skull is fundamentally a pretty good design. A skin covered crash helmet for the brain. Obviously it's not a perfect design or there would've been no need for man to improve on it by designing actual crash helmets for skulls. Other creatures have exoskeletons, so why not an exoskull for us? Anyone who's witnessed torrents of blood cascading from a decent scalp laceration understands what an improvement an exoskull would be.

On the positive side however, not only do skulls protect the brain from injury, they save the head from resembling a jellyfish. Lean back too far in the movies and you'd be staring at the person in the seat behind. Lean forward and people would think you were attempting auto-fellatio.

Skulls are also very cool when depicted on flags and other things by pirates, Mexicans and Jean-Michel Basquiat. Not so cool on the caps of Nazi SS officers, who were definitely the baddies, as ably demonstrated by Mitchell and Webb.

Like being "off your face", you can also be described as being "out of your skull". "Shitfaced" doesn't have a skull equivalent. Although if you skull a few beers you'll probably end up shitfaced. "Shit for brains" means something different and also doesn't mention the word skull.

Ross Faegus (not his real name) had the misfortune of being out of his skull at the wrong time and place and ended up with four holes in his skull. Ross was a professional blackjack dealer at the Sands Hotel and Casino in Las Vegas, where he worked for five years until his untimely death in 1960.

Already a heavy drinker and drug user, Faegus became overwhelmed with the excitement surrounding the filming of Oceans 11 at the hotel, including the performances of the Rat Pack, which became known as the "Summit at the Sands". So Faegus upped his already excessive consumption levels to help calm his over-stimulated mind. Following one of their performances, Sinatra, Martin and Davis chose his table for a few minutes of recreational money laundering.

Faegus was star struck. His hands shook. He turned away from the table and took a large swig of tequila from a hip flask. It proved to be one large sip too many. As he turned back to deal to the stars, the tequila landed in his already heavily taxed stomach, resulting in a projectile vomit of epic proportions, much of which splattered on the chest of Sinatra.

Faegus' naked body was found at dawn in the far corner of the parking lot of the Sands with four bullet holes in his skull and a desert cactus protruding from his rectum. Reports at the time were unclear whether the bullets entered his skull before or after the cactus entered his rectum.

Skull - 7/10 (Good, but could be a lot better.)

SINUSES

Even more so than the nose, sinuses are an absolute disaster. They serve no discernible purpose and the only time you ever become aware that you even have them is when they malfunction. Which they do, for many people, really, really often. Like many times every spring, for example.

The thing that makes allergies such a ridiculous thing is that some people don't have any at all. Others are killed by them. Not only is this crappy design, but a serious quality control issue.

Sometimes sinuses crap out so badly that major surgery, involving drilling holes in the skull, is required to fix them.

Sinuses are all bad. No reason at all for them to exist.

Sinuses - 0/10 (completely pointless)

MOUTHS

The human mouth was designed mainly for cramming food and drink into. Also for talking out of.

Taste buds make food taste good. Which is a good thing. Because if we didn't eat we'd die. It'd be a real shame if we had to shove in fuel that we couldn't stand the taste of, three times a day. The downside is that our taste buds often make food taste too good . The percentage of overweight people indicates that this feature could do with a little fine tuning. And wouldn't it have been so much better if fresh fruit and vegetables always tasted better than a burger and fries? Why didn't the designer make our taste buds crave the healthiest foods? And dislike the opposite. Why design taste buds that crave sugar and fat and salt, to the extent that most people have to exercise serious restraint just to stay healthy?

Food snobs like to claim that their taste buds work better than other people's. That they're more refined. It's one of those claims that works, because nobody can prove otherwise. Most foodies are also wine snobs, so they also claim to have noses that function at a more refined level.

Many people are intimidated by the idea of having taste buds that don't work as well as the experts'. Some people have even been conned into thinking they need a ridiculous looking fat fuck in a cravat to tell them what tastes good. Even if most people need a bit of late childhood encouragement to learn to appreciate broccoli, pumpkin, mushrooms, coriander, caviar, oysters and the like, the only real qualifications needed to become a foodie or wine snob are money, and an ability to learn and repeat words.

Wine snobs are very good at running off a list of fruits, trees, dirt, butter, flowers, meat, leather and all manner of other things that one hopes aren't actually present in the wine. They can often taste ten or twelve of these flavors in a single glass. Yet they're notoriously reluctant to engage in blind tastings. Some wines exhibit traces of cat piss (most sauvignon blanc for example), artificial candy flavors, zinc, plastic and sugar. Buying wine packaged in glass is helpful for avoiding such flavors, though it's not a guarantee. Buying higher priced wine reduces the risk, but it's still no guarantee.

Mouths often fail when using them for their primary purpose. Which is eating food.

Sometimes we bite our tongues, or the inside of our cheeks. Which is an obvious symptom of poor design. Ice cream can result in an instantaneous headache, and a cold drink can feel like a needle has been shoved under a sensitive tooth. Hot food is another matter again. A burnt tongue feels like a swollen strawberry that's sort of sensitive but at the same time can't feel or taste anything. A hot drink can also cause a sharp burst of pain from a sensitive tooth. And a hot slice of pizza will often dislodge that little triangular flap of skin directly behind the top front teeth. Which is both painful and annoying. And subsequently impossible to keep your tongue from irritating. Hard toast or crusty French bread can cause lacerations to the ceiling of the mouth cavity.

Any of these mouth injuries, which always take place at the very beginning of the meal, can ruin the whole meal, and sometimes the next one or two as well.

To finish on a positive, the mouth is pretty damn good at giving oral pleasure to the genitalia of others. And for kissing.

Mouth - 5/10

TEETH

Teeth are a pain. Often literally. As well as being a huge nuisance for various reasons - cavities, decay, splits, chips, cracks, gum disease, infections. It goes on and on.

The design task for teeth is to be strong and resilient enough to chew all manner of food. Hopefully for our whole life, as food's a basic requirement for its continuation. But teeth aren't up to the task. We've developed a whole industry just to keep them functioning. Without dentistry, teeth are incredibly vulnerable and would at various times cause pain, and much worse, to almost all of us. Dentistry's expensive and very unpleasant. Yet we endure it because the alternative, living with the unmaintained and unrepaired original design, would be much, much worse.

There's a whole branch of the dental industry that exists to make teeth look prettier, by means of straightening, whitening and capping, because there's a fair chance they'll look ugly unless they're straightened, whitened and capped. Look at photographs of poor people from a few years ago. The smiling ones should have been told to keep their mouths shut. A gaping mouth of crooked, stained and broken teeth, with more than a few missing, is enough to put anyone off their lunch. It's arguably an even worse look than a completely toothless mouth, aka puckered anus face. Or nah.

Teeth fall out and need to be regrown at a young age. Which is a strange design concept. But not as strange as wisdom teeth, which generally arrive long before wisdom itself, and if they stay too long, might deform your jaw, force your existing teeth out of place, or make you commit suicide to end the pain. Wisdom teeth cause problems because there's not enough room for them on the jawbone.

A design no less stupid than arriving home with a new piece of furniture that's too big to fit up the stairs. So you take it to pieces, carry it up, rebuild it and then realize the door won't open.

Perhaps an economy jet full of morbidly obese holiday makers might have been a better analogy. Although you'd need to extract more than four of them to get it off the ground.

Merely biting too hard on an unexpected hard lump, say a portion of peach pit or olive pit, can smash a tooth in half. The resulting pain is often intense. In the days before dental care, that'd sometimes be enough to cause infection and a long and painful death. Tooth related problems used to kill people in their millions. Almost everybody, according to Christopher Hitchens. Sooner or later almost everybody has a dental problem that needs expert attention, so perhaps the best argument against Hitchens' position is that quite a few people died of other things before their teeth got a chance to kill them.

Other things like Genghis Khan, for example. Khan's anger and propensity for violence may well have been caused by a painful tooth infection. His brutality and depredations are thought to be responsible for the deaths of three quarters of the population of the Iranian Plateau, possibly 10 to 15 million people, before their teeth got to them. The exact cause of Genghis Khan's death remains a mystery. Although variously attributed to being killed in action against the Western Xia, falling from his horse, or wounds sustained in hunting or battle, it's just as likely that his demise was the result of an abscessed lower bicuspid. (If you buy into the idea that his anger was caused by a tooth infection, then you could also, at a stretch, attribute those 10 to 15 million deaths to teeth too.)

Before moving away from violence, reconsider the idiot (referred to earlier) who wants to punch you on the nose. If he misses, he might knock one or more of your teeth right out of your head. It happens all the time. Multiple, independent teeth are quite easy to dislodge and are, therefore, a serious design flaw.

What's the purpose of multiple teeth? Unless they're symmetrical and even and white, teeth look crappy. Why the hell isn't there just a single, big, shiny, white, jaw-shaped chomper, top and bottom, made of ultra hard bone or whatever, that won't chip, break, wear or decay. No flossing required, because there are no gaps. Isn't a bird's beak essentially just a mono-tooth top and bottom? And while we're designing the new improved chewing gear, they'd also be virtually self cleaning. A quick wipe of the tongue would do the job perfectly. Not at all difficult to improve the design of teeth.

If you brush your teeth regularly, using a toothpaste that promises 15 different benefits, you still get a build up of plaque that needs to be scraped off with metal hooks. Pretty much the opposite of fun. And what the hell's plaque anyway? Does it grow on the teeth? Does it ooze out of the teeth? Is it a combo of teeth and water like rust? Is it oral coral, or the oral equivalent of soap scum. Whatever it is, toothpastes that promise to stop a build up of plaque are complete bullshit.

Some of them also promise to control tartar. Next thing they'll be wiping out gluten. How can toothpaste claim to be effective against tartar when the last time anyone got Tartars under control was when Genghis Khan's Mongol hordes were in their ascendancy? You can buy cream of tartar in the supermarket, but it tastes lousy on fish. Why it tastes so much better as sauce of tartar than cream of tartar is a mystery. If Hannibal Lecter were to grind up a Mongolian and eat him raw with a mayo based dressing, he may well ask, "Will I get an increase in build up of tartar from Tatar tartare with tartare sauce?"

Teeth - 2/10 (A thoroughly rotten piece of design.)

JAWS

Human jaws, whilst being no match for many animals' jaws (crocodiles, pit bulls, rhinos, cows, etc) are still very powerful, and can easily bite off smaller body parts. John Wayne Bobbitt may spring to mind as an obvious example, but the mind would be wrong. Lorena Bobbit, in fact, used a knife.

The Achilles Heel of jaws is when they're at full stretch. The power of jaws can be overcome by wedging them in the fully open position, where their strength is minimized. This can be demonstrated by placing your finger in the mouth of a yawning cat. (The finger should be inserted sideways, in the style of a piece of leather or stick being placed in the mouth of a cowboy who's having a bullet removed.) The cat will be surprised and back away, rather than moving just a little and biting down harder, thus helping itself to a little finger food, which it could no doubt do, and probably would if you tried this prank once too often. In other words (and this is not intended as a survival tip in the case of an approaching bear), if jaws are held in the fully open position, the biter is rendered almost entirely powerless.

Snotbo Jiggy, a locally infamous rap-reggae-spoken-word performance artist from Notting Hill, found this out to his embarrassment whilst performing on a small stage made from three wooden beer crates on the Portobello Road in 1979. Snotbo's poetic act consisted of obscene rants with props sourced from adult stores, and outlandish outfits designed to "malfunction" to reveal his genitalia, which he seemed to be very proud of for reasons unclear to his audience. The very thick-lensed, black-framed glasses he wore may have had something to do with his over-inflated opinion of his not very private parts.

According to Snotbo, he took his stage name after being repeatedly mistaken for the much more famous and very much more accomplished Jamaican reggae artist Bo Jiggy. Something that actually happened just the once, according to friends, mainly because he was wearing a t-shirt with the slogan "I heart Jiggy Jig".

During his last reported performance, Snotbo tried to encourage the sole female audience member to take part in his act with him. He demonstrated his intention by shoving his microphone, a replica Shure SM58, right inside his mouth. For those unfamiliar with the SM58, they are a commonly used type of professional vocal microphone with a large wire mesh bulb fitted over the mic itself. Exactly how Snotbo managed to get the bulb end fully into his mouth is unclear, but reports say that he had to attend a local emergency room and wait for three hours before doctors managed to dislocate his jaw and remove the microphone. It is not known whether Snotbo continued his career as a street performer after this incident.

The first thing people think of when they hear the word jaws, is a movie. Then they think about sharks. And shark bites. Then it might occur to them that they have one or two jaws right there, just behind their face. The upper jaw's really just one edge of the skull, so perhaps it shouldn't count as a separate thing. Hence one or two.

While those who live with somebody who suffers from clicking jaw syndrome may not agree, there's not too much wrong with jaws. It takes a pretty good punch to break one. And they do a reasonable job of grinding up steak and, most of the time, of holding teeth in place.

Jaws - 7/10 (Good effort.)

BRAINS

The human brain is the big kahuna. The thing we have that no other creature gets anywhere near. Our brains have amazing capabilities. The most amazing ability, and the one that really sets us apart from other animals, is imagination. The power to conceive new ideas out of nowhere. And the power to communicate those new ideas, including abstract concepts to one another. It's what allows us to invent new things, like cell phones and aircraft. It allows us to make up complicated, abstract stuff and hone it into all sorts of different forms, from stories to poems to songs to movies. And all sorts of other things.

But our ability to imagine is also our greatest weakness. People make stuff up. Then tell other people it's true. And the other people often believe them. Because they find it easy to imagine that it is true.

Most of us go through our lives believing all sorts of nonsense that we think is true, but in fact is just stuff that other people have made up. Congenital liars who are also congenial liars are often the most successful and wealthiest people on earth. And regardless of whether they're selling snake oil or a belief system or an ab blaster or a shake weight or something actually useful, believing them is not necessarily a sign of stupidity. Even the most intelligent people can sometimes be sold a pup by a good looking, smiling, bullshit artist.

But a lot of us aren't intelligent. About half of us, depending on where and how you choose to draw that line.

It'd probably work out a lot better for society as a whole if there wasn't such a wide distribution of brain efficacy. As much as we benefit from having the sort of intellectual firepower that can invent things such as nuclear energy, we're dragged down by the morons who really like the idea of using such things against foes. American comedian Ron White deftly and amusingly makes the point that you can't fix stupid. Which is a shame. Many people are almost entirely unaffected by education, explanation, or the written word. One of the serious downsides of this has to do with the effect that has on democracy and elections, but that's beyond the scope of this book.

There's a common misconception that humans only use ten percent of their brains. This is only true for the type of person who repeats such things with sincerity and belief, without ever having had it verified by any credible source. The reason they've never had it verified by any credible source is because it's bullshit. The sort of bullshit someone like Deepak Chopra might excrete.

Deepak Chopra's a perfect example of someone who takes advantage of the common foible of people not detecting bullshit. Following a brief, but typically convoluted rant using many multisyllabic words, Deepak asked Leonard Mlodinow, an eminent theoretical physicist, if he knew what he meant. Mlodinow replied that he understood what all of the words meant, and, with a shrug, elegantly demonstrated that when strung together in the order Deepak had said them, they meant absolutely nothing. A great demonstration of a very smart human brain easily discerning the type of bullshit that fools millions. And earns millions.

Another misconception is that The Great Wall of China is the only man made object visible from space. An average brain directed at this hypothesis should only take a moment to dismiss it as bullshit, yet it is widely repeated. How long would a piece of string have to be for it to be visible from 20,000 feet?

Our brains are only as good as the information we retain in them. Something we have very little control over. Most of us can remember a ditty from a TV commercial from our childhood (usefulness 0/10) yet we can also return from the supermarket without the milk, being the primary reason we went there. It is reasonably common for a person to walk from one room to another and find that when they get there they've forgotten what they came for. If this sort of thing were unusual, the thing known as a list would never have been invented.

As well as having little control over what we remember, brains are also difficult to control in terms of what we think about in the here and now. We walk along the road and random thoughts jump in, completely unsummoned. We try to concentrate on one thing yet something else suddenly seems a lot more interesting and urgent to think about. How we ever get anything done is a mystery.

And then there's procrastination. Which is the enemy of anything ever getting done. Especially writing books.

Which brings us to sanity. When you have a think about some of the dreams you have, it's hard to argue for your own sanity, let alone anyone else's. The most useful appraisal is probably that we're all insane, but some of us are less insane than others. Brains fall down as a piece of design when one considers that a very minor chemical imbalance can destroy a person's whole life. Personality disorders are not uncommon, and almost always result in life long unhappiness, for sufferers themselves as well as those around them. And it gets a lot worse. If you've ever encountered anyone experiencing paranoid delusions you'd curse any designer who made such a state possible. The same can be said of the designer who decided that seizures and brain tumors should be a part of the overall plan.

On the upside, brains are quite excellent in the way they allow us to enjoy art and music and movies and drugs. Much fun can be had with the brain by introducing chemicals to it, such as alcohol, THC and LSD. The most amusing of the brain candies have the apparent effect of expanding the level of consciousness of the brain. The difference between heightened perception and hallucination is hard to discern or explain, but all manner of revelations and understanding of the nature of everything can be experienced. Unfortunately, such a deep level of understanding is pretty much impossible to retain after the fact and absolutely impossible to explain. A bit like the hilarious story that doesn't fare so well in the retelling and eventually winds down to "you had to be there".

Brains - 2/10 to 7/10 (Depending on the brain.)

THROATS

The pièce de résistance of inept design. Well, one of them.

Imagine if you had to be careful every time you put fuel in your car, because if you weren't it could spill into the air intake and make your engine choke, perhaps causing it to fail permanently (as in die) if the spillage were large enough. No car designer would be stupid enough to put the fuel filler and the air intake inside the very same body cavity. Such spillages would be commonplace if they did. Yet the human body has this exact, ridiculous design feature.

Everyone on earth knows what it's like to choke. At the mild end, it's a quickly forgotten cough or two, when a small drop of water goes down the wrong way. At the serious end, most people have at least heard of somebody that needed saving from imminent asphyxia and death by the violent intervention of a nearby savior.

The failure rate of this piece of design incompetence is so high that the inventor of the maneuver designed to save people's lives because of it, became a household name. Dr

Henry Heimlich. Possibly the only non-gymnast to have ever had a maneuver named after him.

Unless you count the Fosbury Flop as a maneuver. Or the Pincer Movement, named after a particularly vile excretion performed by General Pincer on the battlefield of the Somme in 1915. The reek from Pincer's movement was mistaken for a gas attack by the enemy who abandoned their trenches and ran into the waiting guns of Pincer's 2nd division, who had been the first to vacate the afflicted battleground.

The missionary position doesn't count, even as a single component of a more complex routine, as the particular missionary it was named after is unknown.

In 2016, Dr Heimlich, aged 96, personally saved a life for the first time using his own maneuver, when he Heimliched a fellow resident of his retirement home. Although Heimlich's maneuver has saved many thousands over the years, choking's still one of the leading causes of accidental death. According to Wikipedia, "Choking is the fourth most common cause of unintentional injury-related death in the US. Choking due to a foreign object resulted in 162,000 deaths in 2013."

George W Bush was famously reported to have been choking the pretzel one evening in the White House before the report was corrected to say that he had in fact choked on a pretzel. Queen Elizabeth, the Queen Mother, was hospitalized on three separate occasions after trying to eat fish much too quickly. One of her daughters was hospitalized after burning her legs in a hot bath on account of drinking too much gin much too quickly.

Humans eat and drink a few times every day in order to stay alive. Almost unbelievably, the designer came up with a design that involves a certain amount of risk every single time food or liquid is ingested. Getting air into the food hole isn't really an issue (young boys enjoy deliberately using this feature to induce hilarious belching or farting sessions) but food or drink down the air hole can be terminal. As can too big a lump of food down the food hole. It's like a self-destruct mechanism that can activate at any moment. As a piece of design it can be generously described as gross incompetence. Or complete stupidity. There is no conceivable reason for the throat to be designed this way.

The problems with the design of the human throat have been evident right back to Man v1.0. Meaning Adam. He got a piece of apple stuck in his throat and, according to legend, it's been there ever since.

A less common drawback of the same design fault is when a chunder ends up spurting out your nose, burning the snot out of your nostrils on the way. It would have to be in the top ten of most unpleasant things that can spontaneously occur to the human body. If a blocked toilet caused a sewer fountain in the kitchen sink, you'd be justifiably angry with the idiot who designed that pipework. Anyone who's ever experienced the hell of vomit in the nostrils would not hesitate to vote for a separation of lung, stomach and nose pipes.

An obvious example of a more intelligent design of this area is the dolphin. A dolphin's mouth isn't connected to its lungs, so it can't accidentally inhale water, and therefore won't drown. A dolphin can't choke either, because it doesn't need an epiglottis (aka doomsday flap) and therefore has no requirement for a gag reflex.

The nose is fine where it is (we don't need a blowhole on top) but completely separating the air tube from the food and beverage tube would be an obvious and massive improvement to the quality of life of every human being.

Throats - 0/10 (A drunk four year old could have done better.)

NECKS

The neck, especially the bony bit in the middle, is primarily designed for supporting and positioning the head. The neck also serves to route all the tubes and wires to and from the rest of the body.

The main problem with necks has to do with their fragility, as attested to by the common phrase, a pain in the neck. Anyone who's had an actual pain in the neck will agree that it's no joke. If you happen to break your neck, chances are you've run your last marathon and had your last wank. That's because if you break your neck you have a fairly high chance of permanently damaging the wires inside, and without functioning wires, your brain has no way of telling your hands to get a grip.

The human body has soft parts and hard parts, think brains and bones. So why not some strong but flexible parts, like those really tough hydraulic hoses? If all the vital wires ran down the neck and spine inside one or more hydraulic hoses, there'd be a lot more parking spaces available for able-bodied folk near the main entrance.

A long neck is considered to be more attractive than a stubby one, especially on women. Grace Jones and Mike Tyson may be useful as an aid to imagination here. But a long neck is, fairly obviously, more fragile. Jim Jefferies once said that his mum was the sort of woman who could take a punch, and his description of her indicated that her neck was nothing like Grace Jones'.

With respect to fragility, the neck is closely related to the spine. Some would argue that it is in fact merely the top end of the spine.

Necks - 3/10 (Should be stronger.)

BACKS

The human backbone could almost have been the work of legendary race car designer Colin Chapman. Chapman always strived to design a car to be as light as possible. He was reported to have said that the perfect racing car should win the race and then fall to bits on the slowing down lap. Otherwise it was too heavy. Over-constructed. His original Lotus Elan even had a central backbone chassis, not unlike a human spine.

Like Chapman's cars, spines work very well under most circumstances, and they're definitely not over-constructed. Which is what makes them susceptible to injury when doing something as commonplace as lifting a suitcase, sometimes resulting in serious pain that lasts for days, weeks, months or even a lifetime in many cases.

This is a bit unfair on Chapman as most of his cars didn't break. But back problems do occur at some point for most humans. According to the Mayo Clinic, approximately eighty percent of all Americans experience some back pain at least once in their lives. Quite why the good people at the clinic are bothering themselves with statistics like this, rather than concentrating on delicious creamy dressings for BLTs and the like, is difficult to understand.

According to Wikipedia - "The spinal cord cannot ever properly heal if it is damaged... The spinal cord, if broken, will never repair itself and will result in permanent paralysis."

In other words, the human body was designed to automatically heal cuts, scratches, coughs, colds and bruises, even broken bones, provided they're held in place, but the most important part? Nah.

Why the hell not?

In the days before modern medicine a spinal injury would have been a certain death sentence. (A bit like a bad tooth infection.) Arguably that's preferable to the living hell of a life of immobility and dependence, but many would disagree on that.

Maybe the spine needs to be surrounded by a whole lot more muscle and gristle and stuff like hydraulic hoses are made of, to make sure it doesn't crap out all the time. Or, perhaps if backs were designed more like legs, meaning a series of short bones with a ball on one end and a socket on the other, there would be no need for those spongy discs in between the vertebrae to do so much work and cause so many problems. And putting all those sensitive wires inside such a fragile structure seems a bit crazy. The toe wires don't need to be inside the leg bones, so why do they need to be inside the spine?

How Colin Chapman would have approached this particular design challenge is impossible to say as, alas, he shuffled off before anyone thought to ask him.

Suffice to say that the human spine is a seriously crappy piece of design, partially for being so fragile, but mostly for the inability to heal.

Backs - 1/10 (A very weak effort.)

SHOULDERS

The word shoulder is often associated with the word cold and also the word frozen. If you've ever had the cold shoulder, you'll know that it's unpleasant. But a frozen shoulder is an altogether different thing. A different magnitude of hurt. A different order of ongoing pain, discomfort, and inability to sleep on account of aforesaid. These things are part of the frozen shoulder experience. Ask anyone who's had a frozen shoulder what they think of them. As well as being very unpleasant, they're also very common. At least anecdotally.

An enquiry to the Mayo Clinic regarding the statistical frequency of frozen shoulder in the population was not productive. The help desk, which may be in India, advised that they had no information on cuts of lamb, but that creamy dressings of any variety should never be frozen.

Captain Lawrence Edward Grace "Titus" Oates famously scored the hat trick - one cold shoulder and two frozen. Titus (so knick-named for his unwillingness to share breakfast cereals) famously died during the Terra Nova Expedition in Antarctica in 1912. He was notoriously unpopular within the expeditionary party, not only for scarfing most of the muesli, but also for assuming far more than his fair share of names. On that final fateful morning his three companions awoke to find the burlap bag that usually contained the Special K and scroggin mix, was empty. The more modestly named Robert Falcon Scott, consulted with other members of the party, and they resolved that Oates should be sent to Coventry for the rest of the expedition. It is not known for how long Oates endured the silent treatment, before walking from the tent into a blizzard, where both shoulders rapidly lost temperature and he died. Scott and his crew concocted a story in which they declared Oates to be a hero in order to conceal the fact that they'd bullied him to death.

Shoulders - 3/10

ARMPITS

There's very a big difference between men and women in the armpit department. A woman's armpit can often be delightful. The following observations apply to the male pit.

Revolting and often smelly. Very unpleasant to look at. Especially when framed by the armhole of a singlet (aka sleeveless undershirt or wifebeater).

A singlet somehow focuses the attention on unpleasant pits of hair clumped together by sweat that would be far less noticeable on a bare torso. Singlets also make for really ugly tan marks. Any restaurant that allows a man wearing a singlet to be anywhere near the dining area deserves to go bankrupt immediately.

If armpits were hair free, sweat free and sweet smelling, they wouldn't be called pits. They'd barely need a name at all. They'd just be that bit at the top of the side under the arm.

Male Armpits - 2/10   Revolting.

ARMS

Human arms are a perfect length to comfortably reach one's own groin. Therefore, man seems to have been designed from the outset to be able to play with his own genitals. Which he often does. (10/10 so far)

Man got a better design in this area than most creatures. For example, how on earth would a dolphin or a penguin masturbate? Some scholars point out that cats, dogs and similarly flexible mammals can reach their genitals with their mouths, which is arguably a better deal, but given the way small poodles often drag themselves across carpets and attempt to shag visitors' legs, there seems to a fair amount of frustration there which could theoretically be alleviated by auto-fellatio. Add to that the lack of YouTube videos of cats and dogs orally pleasuring themselves, and the human hand-arm combo seems to be the winning design.

The right to bare arms is a contentious topic, mostly because some men believe it bestows on them the right to wear a singlet. There's nothing in any constitution anywhere on earth that guarantees any man the right to wear a singlet. Legislation to ban the male singlet is long overdue.

A coat of arms sounds like something an octopus would have in a closet somewhere in its garden, but in fact it's not apparel of any sort. A genuine coat of arms can only be acquired by a grant of arms from the College of Arms and is an ornately decorated piece of paper.

Arms can also mean weapons. Such as guns. Men who spend too much time in the gym sometimes like to show off their muscular arms, and wit, by flexing their biceps while saying, "Welcome to the gun show." It always gets a smile.

An arms race doesn't involve human wheelbarrows, walking upside down on one's hands or any other from of competitive arm movement. It also doesn't usually involve a finishing line.

Armed to the teeth is a commonly misused expression as it only really applied to Barbary Pirates, who spent many decades boarding unarmed trading vessels with daggers clenched between their teeth to capture slaves and booty. Although the captives were often turned into sex slaves, this is not thought to have anything to do with the origin of the term "booty call".

Arms have far too many uses to list, everything from shoving food in one's mouth to wiping one's backside, and they do most of those jobs very well.

However, a really well designed set of arms and shoulders would allow you to easily wash your back, or give yourself a full back massage after you've finished playing with yourself. Or before.

Arms - 6/10

NIPPLES AND BREASTS

The most notable things about male nipples are negative. They provide bullies with something to pinch and twist and long distance runners often report that they feel like they've had their tits sandpapered.

Marathon runners who've failed to take the required precautions (usually involving tape) can sometimes be seen with blood from their rubbed raw nipples seeping through their singlets. (Do a Google search for marathon nipple bleed if you'd like to feel queasy.) A willingness to endure that amount of agony in addition to leg, ankle, knee and other pain is clear evidence that you have to be crazy to run a marathon. It's basically a long distance, masochistic torture session that ends with the humiliating proof that you're a loser. Unless you're the winner.

Breasts, aka manboobs or moobs in the case of men, are pretty much useless. Breasts on a woman, however, are an entirely different matter.

Nips and moobs - 1/10 (Or if you're not a bully 0/10.)

SKIN

Skin's pretty good. Skin on skin is one of the nicest touch sensations available to the human animal. It's an integral part of the most pleasurable feeling there is. (Unless you belong to a cult with a stupid rule that mandates a sheet with a hole cut in it, just to ensure that you don't have too much fun. What sort of absolute dickheads think up shit like that?)

Skin functions really well most of the time. Unless you go outside. Where you can get burnt by the sun. Which was already there in the sky at the time man was designed, so it's strange that the designer of skin didn't fully take that into account. If the problem can be fixed as easily as rubbing on some SPF 30, why the hell couldn't a layer of SPF 50 just be designed into skin as standard equipment? Elephants don't get sunburn and neither do giraffes.

And why not make everybody's skin the same color, for fuck's sake? That's a whole load of trouble that could have been avoided with one easy modification. Africa may be sunny but zebras are all the proof you need that a designer can make an animal any color at all, regardless of where it lives.

Skin is easily grazed, cut or punctured. While that's not a major issue, as it's also self-healing, it'd be good if it were somewhat tougher. Faster healing would also be good, especially in tropical climes. Maybe instead of taking a week for a cut to heal, it took an hour. Although that may hamper certain criminal investigations, so it possibly warrants further thought.

Unlike many of the modifications and improvements invented by mankind, the cosmetic tightening of old skin is often not an improvement at all. Quite the opposite in fact. And every attempt to fix it seems to make it worse.

Skin diseases. Rashes. Pimples. Boils. Acne. Shingles. Dermatitis. Allergic reactions. Eczema. Skin can be attacked by far too many things which cause it to itch, change color, blister, bleed, seep, flake and peel.

Healthy skin is pretty good. It gets points for being flexible, sufficiently waterproof, and attractive when young.

Should be less fragile and less disease prone.

Skin - 6/10

HANDS

Human hands generally work fairly well. They also seem to be mostly trouble free, although arthritis does its best to stuff up the day to day enjoyment of life for many older people.

Hands are extremely useful. Many would say they are pretty much essential, as the story of "Hands Off" Dillip-Garli clearly illustrates.

Captain Parkes Dillip-Garli of the Royal Fusiliers, had one hand blown off during a re-creation of the Battle of Ypres in 2014. Due to PHGS (Phantom Hand and Glass Syndrome, a rare form of Phantom Hand Syndrome, meaning that he could not only feel his missing hand but could also feel a cold glass of lager in the missing hand) the Captain kept raising his right hand to his mouth, and was bitterly disappointed every time that no lager arrived. The effect was so real that it caused him to have major psychological issues and was the reason he developed a serious left-handed drinking problem. Or it may have been the PTSD. Probably both.

One evening, whilst holidaying in Bali, Dillip-Garli got a hankering for a pickled egg. He was so inebriated that he momentarily forgot he wasn't in his normal watering hole, The King's Arms in Chipping Norton, and proceeded to help himself to an egg, as was his habit. The jar of pickled eggs in the King's Arms is kept in a spot behind the bar roughly corresponding to the location of the blenders in The Handle Bar in Kuta. Unfortunately for Dillip-Garli, a frozen strawberry daiquiri was under construction at that moment. Thinking he was removing the lid of the pickled egg jar, Dillip-Garli actually took the lid off the blender and plunged his hand in. When asked afterwards how he could make such an error, Dillip-Garli described his condition at the time as "completely pissed".

With prompt and expert medical attention, it's possible Dillip-Garli's left hand may have been saved, but the splatter of frozen strawberry daiquiri confused the extent of the damage to the Captain's hand, and he was made to pay for the daiquiri he'd ruined. The Captain consequently insisted on drinking it before he left the bar. This took some time as he now had no functioning hands and he ended up emptying most of the contents of the blender on his shirt.

(There's an urban myth that an Australian man, who, despite wearing a Bintang singlet was drinking frozen strawberry daiquiris, choked to death on the middle segment of Dillip-

Garli's ring finger that night, but that's never been officially confirmed.)

On his return to Blighty, Dillip-Garli's phantom drinking hands caused him to became incapable of looking after himself and he became homeless. But he was not alone, as he joined a group of other inebriated, shell-shocked veterans in a tent town under a flyover on the A40. After initial efforts by the local constabulary failed to force the old soldiers to break camp, Dillip-Garli in a rare moment of clarity, gave a moving TV interview. The next day a support group took up their cause and arrived with a banner and signs. The most prominent of the signs read, "Leave Our Vets Alone" and "Hands Off Dillip-Garli".

The supporters were horrified when they met Dillip-Garli in person for the first time. As they approached him they realised the terrible gaff they'd committed. And so did the TV crew, who this time made sure they got clear shots of the Captain's stumps, which they deftly juxtaposed with the "Hands Off Dillip-Garli" protest sign. Which is how Captain Parkes Dillip-Garli became known to friends and strangers alike as Hands Off Dillip-Garli, a nickname which stuck for the rest of his life. All thirteen weeks of it.

During a big night on the turps, Dillip-Garli wandered away from the oil drum camp fire to take a slash. While struggling with his fly buttons, he inadvertently staggered into the path of an eighteen wheeler, travelling at just a tad over the legal limit.

Most of Hands Off's body was removed from the front bumper of the White Freightliner, 134 miles past the point of impact, after the driver noticed it for the first time as he walked out of a motorway services restaurant wiping traces of double egg, beans and chips from his lips.

Some have claimed the human hand was designed to hold a banana. Or the other way around. There's a pseudo-scientific video demonstration (still available on the internet if you want a laugh) in which Ray Comfort and friend put forward the hypothesis that the banana was perfectly designed for human consumption, ribbed to fit the human hand for maximum holding pleasure, and even fitted with a tear tab top. Ray and friend are probably still repeating this bullshit to the gullible, and taking their money, despite making complete dicks of themselves. Modern bananas, like the one they used to demonstrate their absurd theory, were redesigned by man. They're a genetically modified version of a wild banana which was a hard little knob of a thing full of large seeds and not at all conducive to human consumption.

What the video experts in the aforementioned YouTube video failed to point out was the similarity of design of the banana to the human penis. If the designer hadn't designed the penis to fit the hand just as well as the banana fits the hand, there'd be no need for threats of hellfire and damnation for playing with it. And if the designer had a strong opinion on whether the penis should be inserted into any mouths or anuses, then a design rethink could've cleared up a whole lot of things.

Fingernails are a nuisance. They should be harder, harder than teeth, and never break or crack. And not require maintenance. Imagine if teeth need filing or trimming like fingernails.

Opposable thumbs are supposedly right up there with intelligence and imagination as reasons why man is the numero uno superior beast on the planet. Not only can we invent things, we can also pick them up. And hit other people with them.

Hands are also good for communicating. Especially for the deaf. Many other people use manual communication too. Navy seals and cops have invented a sign language to be used when storming a building full of baddies that mostly seems to indicate, "There are armed and dangerous people behind that door. You go in first." This sign language has been improved on and expanded by actors who signal furiously and meaninglessly before storming into all manner of death traps. If the hero goes in first, there's a very good chance he won't get shot. Not fatally anyway.

Navigators in racing jet boats use a more basic set of hand signing. Pretty much just left and right, although sometimes they sign so vigorously that it confuses the driver who thinks he's been signed to drive the boat into the audience, or turn it upside down, or both, even though there are no officially recognized hand signs for those maneuvers.

You can flash a "thumbs up" which in most cultures indicates that you're feeling horny, or a double thumbs up which means that you're very horny and/or up for an MMF threesome. A thumbs down used to mean it was time for someone to have their head chopped off, but fortunately civilized societies don't do that sort of thing any more.

There are also hand gestures to indicate that the recipient should engage in sexual intercourse with themselves, or that they indulge in masturbation. It seems odd that anyone would need a stranger to tell them that they masturbate, but apparently people do need telling from time to time.

Hands - 7/10 (Good when they're young.)

HEARTS

The word most commonly associated with heart is attack. Heart attacks can occur any time and anywhere. You can be feeling absolutely fine one minute, driving along perfectly at peace with the world when suddenly you lose control of your faculties and crash the car. If you're unlucky enough to be in the wrong place, at the wrong time, in the wrong colored skin, the police will arrive and pepper spray you, taser you, and finally shoot you for failing to obey their instructions. None of these things are helpful if you've just had a heart attack, with the possible exception of being tasered, provided the police officer aims at your chest and calls "clear" just before firing.

Hearts are not only vulnerable to arterially inspired attacks, they can also be broken by emotional distress. Such as when that hottie you've had the unbelievably good fortune of having a relationship with suddenly comes to her senses and finds a bloke in her own league. It's been said that the only way to repair a broken heart is to get right back on the dating horse, but unless you're extremely rich, your chances of replacing the departing hottie with a new one who's also out of your league, are very slim indeed. Unlike most of the contenders you may now be faced with.

Hearts have had more songs written about them than all the other body parts combined, often in conjunction with the soul, which isn't a body part at all when spelled that way. A good knowledge of science, and biology in particular, is not a requirement for writing country songs.

Hearts can be good, big, sweet, generous, and kind. Also lonely, which people sing about often, even though it's the default setting. With the obvious exception of conjoined twins, there's only ever one heart inside any one body, so of course it's going to be lonely.

Aztecs were fond of removing hearts and holding them aloft, but unlike Christiaan Neethling Barnard, they never had any intention of replacing them. As well-meaning as the Aztecs possibly were in trying to please their Gods with ritual sacrifice, it's now obvious that they were misguided and they've all gone away. Which is good news for young virgins, as they can now attend religious services without cowering in fear should the minister cry out, "Lift up your hearts". This doesn't mean they can totally relax in such places, for obvious reasons. There is one other tenuous link between Barnard, nubile women and religion however, as he is reputed to have had a one night stand with Gina Lollobrigida on the same day as he met the Pope.

Arguably the second most important organ after the brain, the heart partly makes up for its susceptibility to failure by being a part that can be taken out and replaced with a new one. Not a brand new one, like a new hard drive, but at least a better one. Younger and fitter without decades of cigarette, booze and burger abuse on the clock.

Hearts - 6/10

ARTERIES

Arteries are the pipelines that transport the rich, healthy, recently re-oxygenated blood from the heart to all parts of the body.

Unfortunately, the designer didn't design any sort of system where these pipes would be cleaned on a regular or irregular basis. So they eventually get a build up of plaque on the inside walls. Which can lead to arterial disease and possibly the sort of car crash described earlier.

Although it's spelt the same way as the plaque that builds up on teeth, regular brushing is unlikely to help get rid of either type. Does plaque serve any useful purpose? Does a wall plaque serve any useful purpose? It may inform you that somebody famous did something, like being born, in that location a long time ago, but how useful is it for you to know that? And how long are you likely to retain that knowledge after you walk away? If all known forms of plaque suddenly vanished would there be any real downside? Does the same apply to tartar? What is tartar? Is it the same thing? If not, what's the relationship between plaque and tartar? Some toothpastes claim to deal with one rather than the other and some claim to deal with both.

According to TV breakfast show experts, food that tastes good is a big contributor to plaque build up. Wouldn't it have been a better design concept to make the healthiest, least plaquey food the food we like the most? And why weren't our taste buds designed to make food that's bad for us, taste really awful? Instead of that, we live inside a body that collects plaque from our teeth to our toes every time we wash down a delicious meal of jumbo burger and fries with six or eight beers.

Arteries - 5/10

VEINS

A useful way to understand what veins do is to think of them as being much the same as arteries, in that they're part of the same blood transport system, but they're over the other side of a dual carriageway. In British people, the blood moving away from the heart uses the artery side, while in the USA it's the other way around. A bit like the water flowing the other way round a plug hole after you cross the equator. In Ecuador, the water just goes straight down. Not many people are aware of that. Apart from Ecuadoreans. Who all know it so instinctively they don't even notice. Imagine their surprise the first time they brush their teeth in one of the hemispheres. Not that brushing their teeth will do anything much to help their plaque problem.

TV traffic updates often say that arterial roads are flowing well, or possibly blocked by an accident or plaque build up, but there's never a mention of problems on the veinerial routes.

Likewise, references to arterial disease are common but veinerial disease is almost never mentioned. At least not in polite conversation. Whether veinerial disease is caused by plaque build up, or if it's even a real thing probably doesn't matter because if your arteries are blocked there's not going to be much traffic going the other way.

Veins - 5/10

LUNGS

Lungs seem to be perfectly decent organs until something goes wrong with them. Which is not uncommon. When something's wrong with your lungs it's worse than almost any other ailment because of the feeling of suffocation. Although most of us have no idea what dying actually feels like, an inability to breath properly certainly wakes up the imagination.

Other creatures have better designed lungs than humans. Birds have lungs that use an entirely different system from ours. Their lungs are circulatory, with the air moving through in one direction only, while ours are more like bellows. Or something like that. It's complicated. But the upshot is that bird lungs are much more efficient. They can extract a lot more oxygen from the same quantity of air. It's what allows some of them to fly really high, where the air's thinner.

If we'd been designed with wings, which of course we should have been, we'd also need bird-style turbo lungs to go with them.

Breathing is reflexive rather than conscious, which is a good thing, otherwise we'd all die in our sleep every night. The breathing reflex in humans isn't stimulated directly by the absence of oxygen, but indirectly by the presence of carbon dioxide. The higher you go, the less there is of both. Which means those who are unaccustomed to high altitudes suffer oxygen deprivation unless they consciously and continuously increase their breathing rate. In other words, we weren't designed to climb mountains. Which is not a design fault. Arguably it's a feature.

Is there a more dangerous, uncomfortable and pointless exercise than mountain climbing? You get to the top, take a photograph, and immediately climb back down again. Because there's absolutely nothing to do when you get there, and if you stay too long you die. The mission can only be judged a success when you arrive back at the place you started. A result that could be achieved by downloading a photo from the internet, setting up a table and chairs and having a nice lunch.

Another downside of having the breathing reflex driven by too much carbon dioxide, is that when we're in a CO_2 heavy atmosphere rather than up a mountain, we suck harder in search of more oxygen, and the more we suck, the more CO_2 we get, thus triggering even more suck and an inevitable death spiral. The other option in such a circumstance would be to breath less. Although the outcome is likely to be similar.

Wouldn't it be better to have separate in and out pipes? Like car engines and bird lungs. As the exhaust gas exits one valve, the fuel gas enters the other. Seems a lot more efficient and would avoid inhaling the just released exhaust. In cars you put the exhaust pipe out the back and the intake at the front. Only an idiot would design an engine with a common inlet and exhaust pipe.

It'd also be better if we didn't need to breath so often. Whales can hold their breath for an hour and a half. Which is plenty of time to exit a burning building or crashed aircraft before choking to death on smoke. And if our eyes weren't so damn sensitive we could even see the exit signs. It also would mean a full synchronized swimming routine could take place without ever breaking the surface of the water. Except for the leg kicks. Which are brilliant. Colorful nose clips would still be compulsory because it wouldn't be the same without them.

Lungs have a few more downsides. Drowning's not at all difficult, although that's just as much down to the inept design of the throat. Lack of capacity and inefficiency are bad, but not often fatal. Pneumonia, bronchitis, emphysema, coughs and colds and diseases of all sorts are pretty much inexcusable. And lungs are not as good at filtering irritants and poisons as they could be.

Lungs - 3/10 (For keeping us alive most of the time.)

SWEETBREADS

Sweetbreads is a strange word that doesn't accurately describe the following group of organs, even when used correctly, which it isn't here.

KIDNEYS

Kidney goes very nicely with steak when baked into a pie, according to many British chefs. Much better than blackbirds, who apparently don't bake at all well and are still able to sing when the pie is opened by the king.

Kidneys are the twin towns of the human sweetbreads nation. They're shaped like beans. Specifically, kidney beans, after which they were apparently named. Like beans, kidneys are sometimes harvested. After harvesting, the donor wakes up, if they're lucky, in an ice bath in a scummy hotel.

In Chinese medicine, (according to Wikipedia) there are two kidney types, (kidney yin and kidney yang), with the Gate of Vitality between them. All of the four kidney energy aspects are essential in growth and development. These four aspects include kidney jing, kidney yin, kidney yang and kidney qi, which, if read aloud from a notebook by Lawrence Tierney, would certainly annoy the hell out of Harvey Keitel. Kidney Jing is the foundation of the yin and yang of all the body's organs but is not related to Rodney King.

Like all of the yin and yang organs, kidneys are susceptible to a huge range of life threatening malfunctions. There are many painful kidney conditions, but Declan Kidney isn't one of them. He's an Irish rugby football coach.

Traditional oriental medicine is beyond the scope of this book, as is nouveau or new faux science. Deepak Chopra would undoubtedly have an opinion regarding the quantum accuracy of the essence of all of the above. If word salad isn't sufficiently uplifting to your soul, you could strive for further insight with the following creation. Muddle two chicken kidneys in a tall jar, confuse with three spoons of pigpen runnymud, infuse with the therapeutic Ayurveda juice of a random stranger, shake well and stare deeply into the resulting cloudy clarity until all is one. If you find meaning and harmony through the creation of this ancient quantum yang medicinal impuree, you may as well drink it.

Kidneys are best known for the production of stones, but not all stones are produced by kidneys. Nobody knows why kidneys produce stones, or what the purpose of them might be. We do know that they cause excruciating pain. If this is their only function, then the designer is clearly an absolute bastard.

Kidneys - 2/10

SPLEENS

Venting your spleen is nothing like opening a tent flap or farting in an elevator. It has nothing at all to do with breathing out or letting any sort of gas out of your body, unless you've just inhaled a whole lot of anger. It means firing off a barely coherent string of expletives because something has upset the calmness centre in your brain. So any venting of the spleen has everything to do with your brain and little to do with your lungs. Or your spleen.

A ruptured spleen is not the same as a vented spleen. A ruptured spleen requires immediate medical attention. If that's not available, you die. Points off for the spleen. Spleens can be removed mostly without risk of death, although people without spleens are prone to get ill more easily. Pneumonia mostly.

The spleen's job is to filter your blood and do other complicated things with your blood cells, although other organs seem to do similar things. And will happily do so if your spleen is removed for any reason.

As already stated for kidney stones, the designer responsible for an unnecessary organ that can cause excruciating pain and kill you is clearly an absolute bastard.

Spleens - 0/10

LIVERS

Liver with bacon in a gravy sauce can be delicious when well made. That has nothing to do with the liver in the human body.

Unless you're a cannibal. In which case they apparently go well with beans, fava rather than kidney.

The liver in the body of a human does all sorts of things to do with filtering and regulating bodily juices. It's one of the most vital organs, and is very large, weighing about a kilogram and a half, about three pounds or so. Despite its size, it does not handle its work very well with respect to alcohol. One of the primary tasks of the liver is to cleanse the body after a few drinks. Otherwise healthy people can complain of feeling a bit "liverish". This means the liver has failed to detox the body of all of the delicious toxins enjoyed the previous evening.

The term Liver Shot is not a short drink made of alcohol and chopped liver, rather it's a deliberate punch to an opponent in the right side of the ribcage. Reportedly very painful and often incapacitating.

The liver is susceptible to so many different disorders and diseases it would make it the most suscepticemic of all organs and glands if such a word existed.

Prometheus was punished by ancient Greek gods for revealing fire to humans. He was chained to a rock where an eagle or vulture would peck out his liver which would then regenerate overnight. This tells us a couple of things about ancient Greek gods. One of which is that they seemed to know that the liver is the only organ in the human body which can regenerate to a significant extent. The second thing is that they were evil bastards, for wanting the punishment of Prometheus to go on for a lifetime, and for wanting to deprive the rest of humanity from all the benefits of fire including warmth, light, and hot and tasty liver and bacon in gravy sauce. We can all be thankful that the Greek gods have gone extinct.

Livers were used by haruspices (haruspex in the singular), a form of charlatan in Ancient Rome, who claimed to be able to read omens from entrails. Fortunately, haruspices have also gone extinct.

Liver-Eating Johnson, a mountain man of the American Old West, reputedly scalped and ate the livers of 300 Crow Indians. It is not known if Hannibal Lecter was a descendant of his, or if he was related to Pear Loving Johnson, Long Toes Johnson or Two Sheds Jackson.

According to Wikipedia, "One tale ascribed to Liver-Eating Johnson was of being ambushed by a group of Blackfoot warriors in the dead of winter on a foray to sell whiskey to his Flathead kin, a trip that would have been over five hundred miles (800 km). The Blackfoot planned to sell him to the Crow, his mortal enemies, for a handsome price. He was stripped to the waist, tied with leather thongs and put in a teepee with only one, very inexperienced guard. Johnson managed to break through the straps, then knocked out his young guard with a kick, took his knife and scalped him, then quickly cut off one of his legs. He made his escape into the woods, surviving by eating the Blackfoot's leg, until he reached the cabin of Del

Gue, his trapping partner, a journey of about two hundred miles (320 km)."

That story doesn't really have much to do with the topic at hand, but it would make a very good movie, being a tale that is both exciting and very much more plausible than The Revenant. Also good is the way that Liver-Eating Johnson took his own good time scalping the hapless guard before "quickly" cutting off one of his legs.

Livers - 4/10

GALLBLADDERS

Gallbladders would get less than zero points if that were possible under the scoring system. Apparently all they do is suck bile from the liver and have all sorts of stuff go wrong with them. Including gallstones, which are incredibly painful, but not as painful as kidney stones or as painful as being stoned to death for breaking a rule some old dickhead made up a long time ago.

Strawberry gallbladder (aka Cholesterolosis) is just one of the many things that can go wrong with the gallbladder. It's almost certainly very painful and would probably look like a severely burnt tongue.

The worst (or best) thing about the gallbladder is that you can have it surgically removed, usually without any harmful effect. In other words, it's as useful as an unemployed, abusive husband. It sits around all day, doing bugger all, just waiting for something to upset it, so it can cause you pain.

Like many of the sweetbreads, the gallbladder is a hopeless piece of design, easily improved by just getting rid of it. Horses, deer, rats and many birds don't have them. Bears wish they didn't have them, because then total arseholes wouldn't keep them in cages and stick tubes into them to suck out their bile.

The gallbladder gets its only point because if you become the victim of an organ thief, it won't be your gallbladder's fault. Market value - nil.

Gallbladders - 1/10

ALIMENTARY CANAL

STOMACHS

Your stomach reminds you of its existence every time you want something to eat. Or if you've had too much to eat. Or drink. Sometimes, if you've had too much to eat and too much to drink, your stomach will wake you in the night and insist on being emptied. Immediately. Via the mouth. A common reaction is to try to suppress the message, but a wise gourmand, or experienced trencherman, knows the benefits to be reaped from a good chunder in the wee small hours.

The stomach is where breakfast starts to be transformed into energy and nutrients useful for the body to function. Within an hour or two, breakfast no longer resembles liver, bacon or eggs and has become chyme. Which is a pleasant sounding word until you imagine what it would look and smell like. Very unpleasant. Like the sound of church bells chiming at the crack of dawn after a big night on the turps.

The average human stomach can comfortably contain about a liter of food. Think about that next time you sit down to a large vindaloo having already poured about six or seven pints of lager in there. For those who have trained their stomachs to hold many liters of food, a solution can be to have a rubber band applied to it.

The stomach loses points for sending signals to the brain that more food would be appreciated, even if, probably especially if, you're already carrying around more than a sensible amount of flesh and fat.

Stomachs sometimes object to being in the wrong country. They indicate their displeasure by utilizing an arsenal of pain, vomiting and explosive diarrhea. Often with little to no warning. Locals consuming exactly the same things have no such issues. The designer was clearly an unimaginative imbecile who did not anticipate international travel when designing the stomach.

Stomachs are usually thought of as being the place where the digestion happens, but most of it actually occurs further down the tract.

Stomachs - 3/10

SMALL INTESTINES

This is where most of the digestion happens. Most of the digestion that actually occurs that is. Up to fifty percent of what we shove in our mouths eventually comes out the other end. Or elsewhere. (It's hard to find an accurate figure on this, so it's a fairly broad approximation. But close enough, given that the ideal figure is zero.) Which makes the small intestine a contender for worst designed of all organs. That it was not designed to digest one hundred percent of what we eat is crazy. If it could do that we'd have no need for toilet paper. Or toilets. Or a large intestine, colon, rectum or anal sphincter. Or any of the shit that goes with all that stuff, including diseases. And shit.

Shit is horrible stuff. Yet we have a body designed to produce shit every day, so we have to deal with shit every day. Sure we get used to it, but if you could opt out of ever having to take a shit again, would anyone opt in? The reason that taking a piss or a shit can seem enjoyable is because it's the only way to put an end to gradually increasing discomfort. It's the same reason people smoke cigarettes. And just as nobody has a cigarette because it's so enjoyable (oh stop lying), nobody is going to say, look I just took a shit five minutes ago, but it was so lovely I wish could take another one right now. Or, I like crapping so much, I wish I could crap ten times a day.

Trees can absorb energy from the sun, and nutrients from the rain and the ground, and grow and live for a hundred years without ever once needing to take a crap.

Electric cars can be charged with energy from the sun and go much faster than a cheetah, without ever needing to take a piss or a shit.

So why should we have to?

Why can't we have a digestive system that's totally efficient so that every single part of what we eat and drink is utilized by the body as nourishment or energy? It's what already happens to half what we shove in our mouth holes, so why not all of it? Same system, just better. More efficient. Everything processed into what we need. No waste. Problem solved. Assholes gone. Not required.

And we wouldn't need to deal with all the shit that goes wrong down there. Like constipation or explosive diarrhea. Or haemorrhoids. That's all taken care of with the new design. No more shitting, no more pissing. No more poo on the finger when the toilet paper's missing. Or too flimsy.

It has been pointed out that if you spread out the small intestine, you could cover a tennis court with it. Or eight football fields. Why on earth this matters to anybody is a mystery, as it's unlikely to be a good playing surface. Also a mystery is whether anybody's actually tried to spread organs on playing fields in this manner, but it might be a nice way to get a deceased friend or relative into the Guinness Book of World Records.

The small intestine is a yang organ in traditional Chinese medicine. Which is either a good thing or a bad thing. Deepak Chopra would know the answer. Or at least he'd keep talking until some words tumbled out that sounded like they might be an answer to something. Or a deeper question.

The list of things that can go wrong with the small intestine is long, and includes vile things like tape and hook worms, and cancer, but it makes no difference because the design score is already zero. As it is for everything further down the tract.

Small Intestines - 0/10 (a hopelessly inefficient organ)

APPENDIX

The appendix is like a doggy bag attached to the connection between the small and large intestines.

The jury's still out on whether the appendix does anything useful. Or, like some of its sweetbread cousins, anything at all, apart from cause trouble. It's most well known for its ability to develop appendicitis, a painful condition that can strike any time without any sort of warning and kill you dead. Unless there's somebody handy with a knife who can cut you open and remove the troublesome organ. The only significant side effect of an appendectomy is that you can't get appendicitis again.

Perhaps the appendix was useful to the aforementioned haruspices who may have been able to find footnote references and other information too detailed for inclusion in the rest of the entrails.

Appendix - 0/10

PANCREAS

Anatomically speaking, the pancreas is divided into the head of pancreas, the neck of pancreas, the body of pancreas, and the tail of pancreas. Which sounds like we have an alien body living inside us. But it's really just another sweetbread, another chapter in the book of entrails. And another one that can kill us for no reason. The pancreas is indeed most well known for setting off life-threatening medical emergencies.

Pancreas - 0/10

LARGE INTESTINE

COLON

RECTUM

SPHINCTER

These are all components of a system that should not exist at all in a well designed creature.

LI, C, R, S, etc - 0/10 (Totally unnecessary, see above.)

ANUSES

Having a crap. Taking a shit. Number twos. Doing jobbies. Layin' a cable. Takin' a deuce. Apart from a momentary sensation of relief, it's not fun. Especially not in the days before toilet paper and indoor plumbing.

Taking a shit and giving a shit are entirely different things, the latter not involving excrement at all. Unless the shit's being given in a flaming paper bag left on somebody's doorstep. Holy shit isn't a slang expression meaning consecrated bread or sacramental wine and holy piss isn't a thing.

While we usually think of the dual nature of our bottom end waste, there are in fact three components. Solid, liquid and gas. The solid and liquid components have their own exit tubes, but the gas shares its exit with the solid matter. Which can lead to accidents, aka skid marks, in the tighty-whities. Or worse. If things are not all well down below, perhaps there's been some curry consumption or a sip of water in the wrong country, an attempt at a subtle release of gas can result in a mess. Very unpleasant for all concerned.

Occasionally the sphincter decides to stop the music before the party's over, snapping shut mid turd. Or trying to snap shut. It doesn't matter how many slices of TP you use, it always seems to need one more wipe. Sooner or later you just have to give up or you'd end up wiping your arse until it was red raw like a runny nose. Not a great piece of design.

The world's fourth biggest selling product by volume is haemorrhoid cream. Could the massive haemorrhoid cream industry exist solely because of a piece of really crappy design? Apparently, yes. There are lots of other industries that also exist to compensate for bad design. Optometry, dentistry, footwear, designer sunglasses, hats, toilet manufacturing and breast augmentation readily spring to mind.

On the bright side, farts are arguably the funniest things a child can ever encounter. Any reference to opening your lunch box, cutting the cheese, breaking wind, doing a windypop or imitating the sound of a fart is enough to make most children howl with laughter. It's said that the average person farts 14 times a day, although hard-drinking, sausage-scoffing men who can exceed that by orders of magnitude can be readily found on any German building site.

A brave fart is an expression unknown outside Scotland, and is more likely to involve a red face than a blue one. It means attempting to let a fart whilst running. It is indeed a brave feat, although foolhardy, as a successful completion is definitely not easy. Marathon runners and race walkers sometimes try to sneak one out near the finishing line just to have it go horribly wrong. The internet carries numerous photos of the evidence of miscalculation splattered all down the backs of athletes' legs.

If running has the effect of softening, and possibly liquefying, even a brick hard stool after an hour or two, then entering a marathon should be a certain cure for constipation. For most people a few pints of Guinness and a vindaloo would be preferable treatment.

Of all the human body parts that we'd be happier without, the anus would have to be it. As previously mooted, if our digestive organs worked at 100% efficiency to produce no waste, our lives would be massively improved. And fundamentalist American politicians could save an enormous amount of time and money not having to make up lots of silly laws about who could use public conveniences.

Anuses - 0/10

EXCRETION

Most of this subsection is sufficiently covered elsewhere, especially given the stated subject of the book, and it's largely a digression, so it should probably be skipped over by everybody. Except perhaps by those who haven't quite grown out of being childishly amused by poos, wees and farts.

Sometimes the need to take a dump is so urgent that you have to stop what you're doing and take one immediately. Especially if you've eaten something that your system rates as hard to stomach. You may be watching the exciting climax of a great TV drama or sporting event, when suddenly you feel that you really need to go to a tiny room and make a big smelly mess. And then clean it up.

But that's not so bad compared to the guy driving along a highway in Australia who felt the need to unload an urgent shidooby. He stopped his car and dashed behind a tree. His feeling of relief was brief. Fangs in the wanger and a snake covered in shit. They don't call it the Deadly Hume for nothing.

In times gone by there were performers with established acts that relied on their ability to fart on cue. Sometimes quite musically it was claimed. They often performed their works of flatulence in places of opulence such as grand country houses and royal courts. Royals used to drink more back then, at least in public, and didn't bother too much about feigning maturity.

Joking about faecal matters can be the opposite of funny. On a hot summer day in 1973, Marty Link of Wanganui, New Zealand, famously decided to perform a prank in the Gonville Municipal Pool. He took a Cadbury Picnic Bar from its wrapper, secreted it in his hand and dived into the pool, releasing the rough-surfaced chocolate log on entry. Shortly after Marty exited the pool, the cry went up. There's a poop in the pool! Brown trout, brown trout, everybody out!

There was agitation in some parts and laughter in others, but on one thing there was consensus. No more swimming. Even Marty and his idiot prankster friend Georgie knew they couldn't dive in without becoming suspects. Most people had already left by the time the janitor netted the "chocturd" and revealed its confectionary nature.

Among those who went home early were Miriam Knobbs and her two young children. Miriam's husband, Johnny, three quarters of the way through a bottle of Jim Beam, was surprised by their early return. Very surprised. He was masturbating to printed images of a thoroughly unhealthy, and in fact illegal nature when they walked in. Miriam was horrified.

Johnny Knobbs was arrested in a seedy motel four days after the bodies of Miriam and the children were discovered. Marty Link and his idiot friend, Georgie, were called to testify at the trial. They denied all knowledge. Which was very nearly true given their academic achievements to date. When questioned afterwards by reporters they refused to answer but as they walked away they were heard giggling and saying words like shidooby and floater. Such is the way of the prankster.

Johnny Knobbs' lawyer tried to load some responsibility on the stupid boys, but if you're going to rewind a butterfly effect like that, where do you stop? You may need to consider going all the way back to the very existence of the totally useless and unnecessary thing known as the human turd.

Depending on where and what you've been eating, turds come in many varieties, from sphincter-tearing coal-hard logs, to chocolate peanuts to projectile liquid eruptions and everything in between. In fact, at the liquid end of the scale they can no longer really be categorized as turds. More like fecal porridge. Traditionally known as a wet fart, or a wetty, the word shart has been recently coined to cover the brown area between a shit and a fart.

Sometimes you get the feeling that a wetty might be on the way so you decide to hold all gas until you find a reasonably sanitary toilet. Other times that's not a practical option and you're forced to try a gentle test release. If you're a long way from home, a test fart can have very unpleasant consequences. What's worse is when you feel certain that you're priming a 100% gas, perfectly dry, safely releasable fart, but then, disaster. It's neither dry nor safe. A nasty little design feature. Anyone who's ever been caught a long way from home after eating something that reacts violently knows of the horror of a surprise shart.

White underpants were invented by Marcie Giuliani in 1934, as a way to control the behavior of her wayward teenaged sons, both of whom were on the fast track to delinquency. When young Rudi called his mother a stupid bitch in front of his friends, Marcie promptly fetched his heavily skid-marked tighty-whities and showed them to the gathering. "Rudi, Rudi,

Rudi, Rudi," she said. "Your mouth's almost as foul as your bottom. You should try to get both of them under control." Hilarity ensued, along with humiliation in equal measure. From that day on, Marcie's boys always treated her with respect.

Marcie Giuliani divorced her husband the following year, reverted to her maiden name, Hanes, and started a successful underwear company.

Number Twos - 0/10

BLADDERS

The human bladder is also known as the pissack. As distinct from the nutsack or ballsack which hangs beneath it, and the cossack, which has nothing to do with either, unless one has been drinking vodka. The bladder has a theoretical capacity of between 300 and 500ml, although it's not terribly unusual for people on a Friday evening to nail twelve or fifteen standard drinks in quick succession. Sometimes more. So it must be fairly flexible.

We begin our lives with no control over our bladder and often, unfortunately, end our lives the same way. Diapers or nappies thus come in various sizes for babies, seniors and astronauts on transcontinental murder missions that may involve incontinence. Incontinence is the opposite of transcontinence, which is the ability to travel from coast to coast without a bathroom break.

A design which requires a young animal to undergo toilet training to avoid making a stinking mess all over the place would be easy to improve on. In fact if such a thing did not already exist and someone came up with a design of an animal whose offspring would naturally, and without instruction, decorate themselves and their surroundings with shit and piss many times a day, that person would be declared a perverse fool rather than an intelligent designer.

Urination, pissing, peeing, tinkling, piddling, micturition, voiding, uresis, emiction, weeing, whizzing, having a slash. There are lots of words for this necessary activity that happens to be a lot less hassle for men than for women, in most situations. Probably the reason that we have lots of words is because we have to do it so bloody often. Up to seven times a day is considered normal for this nuisance of an activity.

Micturition becomes necessary a lot more often if one indulges in a serious session of drinking alcohol. This is why binge drinking is also known as "getting on the piss". Another disadvantage of flying into the turps is that sometimes in the middle of the night men find themselves voiding their bladder into the darkness of a stranger's wardrobe. The downside of this is of course far greater for the stranger who was drunk enough to let the offending pisshead into their house.

Although firmly in the category of things we'd be better off without, pissing is nowhere near as bad as shitting. In fact, an outdoor piss under the stars is often quite enjoyable. Although not as enjoyable as a drink under the stars. Or a shag, pretty much anywhere.

For some people "drinking piss" isn't a slang term for having a few beers. They actually drink piss. Real actual piss. Under the guise of "urine therapy". Urine therapy involves drinking urine or rubbing urine onto your skin and gums. Usually your own urine. "Shivambu Shastra", has been respected for thousands of years as the "Mother of Ayurvedic Medicine" and is commonly known as "Self-Urine Therapy". The human body's waste liquid apparently contains "essential nutrients, natural vaccines, antibacterial, antiviral and anticarcinogenic (sic) agents as well as hormone balancers and allergy relievers". Why would the human body feel the need to expel such goodness many times every day? What may be self-evidently ludicrous to some, becomes "truth" to others, apparently on the basis of being thousands of years old and incorporating exotic foreign words.

There is a belief that drinking tiger urine and rhino urine is guaranteed to make you fitter and stronger and younger than anyone you want to compare yourself to. The catch is that for rhino and tiger urine to be effective, it must be collected from unharmed specimens in the wild. Spreading the catch part of this belief will have the double benefit of saving the lives of these creatures and reducing the numbers of poachers.

There's no scientific evidence to support any of the wacko claims associated with urine therapy. Its only benefit seems to be that, like eating competitions and body piercing, it provides TV shows with regularly repeatable gross-out entertainment. At least once a year breakfast TV shows wheel out a couple of nut jobs who are happy to drink their own piss live on TV. Eeeeew.

The common term for urine, piss, has arguably the most variations and uses of any word in the English language. And most of them don't involve urine in any way.

You can tell someone to piss off, which can mean go away or merely that you don't believe them, neither of which has anything to do with being pissed off. Americans just say pissed when they mean pissed off, but pissed without the off actually means drunk. It can be pissing down outside, while two men indulge in a pissing contest in the board room. One of them might be a piss head, and the other may be a piss ant, who may also be piss weak. Pissing up a flagpole may be a waste of time but it's not as bad as pissing into the wind. And taking the piss is not the opposite of pissing something away. Piss poor has nothing to do with urine or poverty.

So we'd still have plenty of uses for the word piss in the event of a redesign that makes urination unnecessary.

As with all the other organs there's a long list of malfunctions and diseases that can occur in this department.

Bladders - 0/10 (Get rid of 'em. Alternatively, a mild orgasm as a reward for each pinkle may make it worth keeping.)

PROSTATES

Prostate should not be confused with prostrate, prostitute, proboscis, perineum or politician. Although they're mostly unrelated, it wouldn't take long to think up a tongue-twister utilizing all those words.

The prostate is another candidate for the title of absolutely shittiest piece of design in the whole human body. It combines two totally separate and, for most people, unrelated functions, urinating and fornicating, into one organ or gland. Some people have found ways to enjoyably combine these activities, but researching the topic may lead you to stumble across something called Omorashi in Wikipedia (warning - do not look it up) so it's better just to leave that and move on.

The prostate is the exact opposite of a design with inbuilt redundancy. Redundancy can mean using more words than necessary. See the rest of this book for many examples of that. Redundancy in the design sense means having a back up system for reliability of operation. If an army helicopter or jet fighter cops some flak in one side, there's a duplicate, or redundant, set of wiring on the other side allowing the machine to keep flying. The prostate is more like a system where if the plane is struck in one wing tip, an inbuilt explosive charge blows the tail off the plane. Seriously and dangerously stupid design. No exaggeration.

The prostate is utilized by some people for sexual stimulation. This usually requires inserting something up one's backside. Suffice to say that some people seem to like it, so good on you if that's the case, messy though it may be.

Even though it was hopefully not designed with this in mind, the prostate's number one claim to fame is as an incubator for cancer. We all know and respect the phrase, "use it or lose it", and this seems to be the case for the prostate. Current medical thinking recommends that men should have as many orgasms as possible, preferably at least one a day, for their whole life, as a way of maintaining a healthy prostate. Which seems to make sense. Other parts of the body benefit from exercise. Although not going for a walk doesn't result in cancer of the leg, so the consequence of not beating the meat on a regular basis seems a little harsh.

This advice contradicts traditional religious teaching on the subject of jerkin' the gherkin, but that's not a topic for this book. Except to observe that going blind and stropping the mulligan have as little in common as excellent health and drinking your own piss.

Prostate - 0/10

GENITALIA

Genitalia and waste disposal should really be separate topics but they keep on merging and getting a bit messy. As previously discussed, that's exactly how they're designed.

The throat was an early candidate for the Palme d'Or of inept design. However, the combination of the exhaust pipes and the sexual organs is breathtaking in its stupidity.

Neil deGrasse Tyson said it's like building an amusement park right next to a sewage treatment plant. Actually it's worse than that. It's like building the rides right inside the plant, with the log flume ride splashing through the settling ponds.

Why would you put something that's fun to fondle with hand and mouth, right next to something that's the opposite of fun to be near? Meaning faeces, turds, shit, piss and poos. Okay, faeces may be fun to play with in terms of flinging shit around the asylum or hurling turds through the bars at your human cousin jailers, but for most of us, shit is a very unpleasant thing to have to deal with.

Putting that aside for now, let's consider the upside of genitals. The act of sex. It's fun. Really good fun. Maybe too much fun. It seems like a crazy thing to say, but when men spend 83% of their waking and 92% of their sleeping time thinking about sex, perhaps the dial doesn't need to be turned all the way up to eleven. If it was turned down to one, it would probably be enough to ensure the continuation of the species.

A scientist reportedly once said that only 1 in 387,000 acts of sexual intercourse resulted in the birth of a child. When you add the average lifetime tally of masturbation to that figure, it becomes obvious that the dial could be turned down a long way without extinction through lack of procreation becoming even a remote possibility. (Unlike Pandas. They neither give themselves hand jobs nor auto-fellate, yet they can't be bothered having sex more than about once a decade. Their dial is turned down much too low. Although, they don't seem to kill each other in fits of jealousy, so maybe they're happier that way.)

Perhaps if the actual pleasure factor went up, but the required frequency went down? We'd all get a lot more done if we only thought about it once a week. But could the pleasure factor be dialed up? The existence of performance enhancing and recreational drugs indicates that it could. Many people have reported that chemically enhanced pleasure really is a thing. There are almost certainly scientists and others out there working hard on the topic right now. Lots of fun. Points in the bag.

Human sex seems to be more fun than it is for most other animals. It's a lot better than the sex life of a praying mantis, for example, or of the water dragons that sometimes fornicate in plain view on river banks. They seem to enjoy it well enough, though it only lasts a few seconds. Including foreplay. Which could be described as a running jump ending in a half nelson. The main event involves a static vice-like grip promptly ended by three mat slaps and a quick dismount.

Genitalia - 8/10 (Should really get 0/10 on account of the huge hygienic design bungle, one of the biggest design fuck ups in the whole human body, but they are a lot of fun.)

Coitus - 5/10 - 10/10 (It varies.)

TESTICLES

Testicles was not a Greek philosopher. He was a Greek poet. Famous for being the worst of all the Greek poets. Testicles, the body parts, were named after Testicles the Greek poet because most Greek citizens, if offered the choice, would rather take a swift kick to the nuts than sit through a long and tedious poetry recital by Testicles.

A gentleman's bollocks hang down between his legs in a sack that offers all the impact protection of a sheet of soggy toilet paper. Which is crazy, as the nuts themselves are as sensitive a body part as anyone would ever care to imagine. Even a mild impact or gentle compression of the plums, is enough to make a man's eyes water. And a decent kick in the nads will drop any man to the ground and have him writhing in agony for some time. Delicate organs, permanently swinging in the breeze, constantly at risk of accidental knocks or squishing is an obviously stupid design fault. So, why are they hanging out like that? The reason they need to be on the outside, apparently, is that they only function correctly a few degrees below core body temperature. So they need to be air-cooled. Seriously.

What genius would design a body part that didn't function properly at body temperature? And then come up with a sack as a solution to the problem. It's as clever as an outhouse at the bottom of the garden.

What makes it completely ridiculous is that it's so very easily fixed. Make them operate at body temperature, like every single other organ, and put them inside. Out of harm's way. (To look on the bright side, I guess we're lucky our kidneys and lungs aren't hanging out below our armpits.)

Human testes initially develop inside the abdomen. Later, during gestation, they migrate through the abdominal wall into the scrotum. This causes two weak points where hernias can later form. Prior to modern surgical techniques, complications from hernias, such as intestinal blockage and gangrene, usually resulted in death. Another great feature of this total design abomination.

Sloths, elephants, anteaters and birds are just some of the many animals with internal testicles. Which obviously work perfectly well at body temperature. So there's no excuse for this design stupidity. Or is it worse than mere stupidity? Is it deliberately sadistic? Why the hell are they so bloody sensitive?

The male tuberous bush cricket, Platycleis affinis, has testes that account for 14% of his body weight. It's a good thing for Jiminy that his plums are inside, rather than hanging out in the breeze. If a man's nuts were of the same proportion, there'd be a couple of rugby balls flailing around his knees.

Which is nothing compared to Viz comic book hero, Buster Gonad, the boy with unfeasibly large testicles. During a storm, Buster's gonads were zapped by cosmic rays which enlarged them to an enormous size. Buster's gonads are so big he has to use a wheelbarrow to go for a walk. True fact.

Balls on the outside - 0/10 (Stupid beyond belief.)

PENISES

Size. It matters. Of course it does. Things need to fit in order to work properly. So why is there such a large variance in size? It seems that the majority of penises fall within a normal size range of small, medium and large, but there are a number in the categories of tiny and huge. A competent designer would engineer in some quality control to ensure that there was a small maximum deviation from a perfect size. Design tolerances have already been discussed. They should also be applied here. And everywhere else for that matter. Nobody likes being too unusual. The fact that the categories tiny and huge even exist, is not the work of a good designer.

Despite that it's fair to say that the penis is easily the most fun part of a man's body. But it really does seem like a dumb idea to use the same thing we use to expel malodorous waste from our body, to put inside someone else's body. Shouldn't there be two separate appendages for this? Or preferably, as previously discussed, everything we consume should be processed into energy, therefore not needing a piss tube at all.

Penises - 9/10 (Because they're really good fun.)

MORE ON HAIR

There's no conceivable reason for having hair in the butt crack. It's definitely not a positive contribution to hygiene. One of the accepted reasons for the existence of hair is warmth, but for a body part that's as much inside as out, that's hardly an issue. Heads get cold. Arms, hands, fingers, feet, even eyes sometimes, but butt cracks? No. Hair in the butt crack could be a real pain in the ass, if it were more than a mere annoyance.

While we're in the area, the reason for hair on the balls is what exactly? It can't be to keep them warm because the reason they're hanging out there is they need to stay cool. And the amount of hair on the average nut sack would never qualify as fur. It's a garnish, or decoration at most, inconsequential. And, unlike butt crack hair, it's not even annoying. It's just silly.

Moving on to the short and curlies surrounding the penis. A palm tree growing out of a big bushy thicket appears to be somewhat shorter than a palm tree growing out of bare sand, so pubes aren't there for the sake of making a man look impressive. Surely the designer wouldn't have created an area just for crabs to play?

Sex on the beach is one of those things that seems idyllic, but in practice, there's sand. Sand is pretty much the exact opposite of a lubricant. And so is short and curly hair. Sometimes, when doing odd jobs around the home, sand paper is the best abrasive, other times a ball of steel wool works better. Some people have suggested that porn stars go Brazilian to appeal to pedophiles, but it's probably for more practical, friction reduction purposes. After all, if they were really trying to appeal to pedos, they wouldn't spend all that money on big fake titties.

A pube stuck between the teeth is sort of funny, but it's also the sort of laugh we could easily do without. And wouldn't miss. An unruly bush not only gets in the way of threesomes and twosomes, but also of onesomes. Many people apparently go right through life without discovering the benefits of having a larger low-friction play area.

Pubic Hair - 0/10

HIPS

Hips are a reasonable design in that they allow us to walk and run and sit down and even swim. But often they're a source of pain, much like backs and necks and knees. As with eyes and other parts, they tend to give trouble as we age. And the older we get, the more likely we are to break one. Or to require new, surgically-installed components.

Snapping hip syndrome is not necessarily age related, nor is it related to clicking jaw syndrome. It's sometimes painful, but sometimes not. In which case an early onset sufferer may frequently turn around expecting to see a turtle at their heels, not realizing that the snapping sound is coming from within. If it's not diagnosed within a reasonable time frame, the sufferer of snapping hip syndrome may end up needing psychiatric as well as medical care.

Hips have long been associated with sex and sexiness. The variation in shape between men and women has a lot to do with this. Also their proximity to the fun bits. When someone uses exaggerated hip movements while performing a song and/or dance it is often criticized as being provocatively sexual. Elvis

Presley, aka "Elvis the Pelvis", was accused of vulgarity and animalism, and headlines such as "Beware Elvis Presley" and "lock up your daughters" were not uncommon as parents and community leaders became terrified of the prospect of rampant juvenile delinquency. At one time Elvis was filmed by police, for evidentiary purposes, and threatened with jail for his wiggling hip moves. Juvenile delinquency was apparently cured, or just ceased being a thing, some time after the Hippy Hippy Shake Shake slid from the charts.

Modern variations of shaky hip dancing, such as twerking, have taken it to new levels of debauchery. For those not familiar with recent music videos, it mostly resembles a mime performed by scantily clad young ladies bending over whilst being vigorously rogered by another performer or by an imaginary 800-pound gorilla with Parkinson's disease. If community leaders still abhor such behavior, they either keep it mostly to themselves or they've lost touch with the media. Or with their communities.

Hip hop has very little to do with hips or hopping. How it came to be called hip hop is a mystery.

Hips - 7/10 (Fine while functioning correctly.)

BUTTOCKS

The current popularity of big butts, or more correctly, massive butts, is bewildering to some, but there was a time when ladies were bound into tight corsets before being inserted into wire-framed skirts that gave the impression that there was a huge butt lurking beneath the fancy fabric. What's changed is that bum flaunting is now performed without the camouflage of a portable yurt. Which means that many young women turn to cosmetic surgery, indicating that the original design they were born with is unsatisfactory in their eyes.

Cosmetic surgery of this nature is often performed by people who are not qualified surgeons, because surgeons charge too much, and because they usually have more sensible things to do. Non-surgeons are also less restricted in the variety of things they can cram into their naive customers' butts. Instead of silicon implants or injections of fat harvested from other parts of the body, the SMCAA (Scummy Motel Cosmeticians Association of America) recommends injecting compounds that contain cement, super glue, cornflour, pulverized ramen noodles and pretty much anything else that springs to mind. It's almost certainly a better idea just to eat the noodles and cement and let them make their own way to your butt.

As crazy as it seems to run the risk of having your bum fall off in pursuit of sexual attractiveness, ridiculously inflated buttocks are by no means the riskiest of fashion-driven body mods. Eyeball tattooing is actually a thing. When that goes horribly wrong (and really, what other outcome is likely?) and you can't see any more, at least you can feel more sexually attractive because you can imagine that anybody hitting on you is a ten. Of course they won't be. Tens don't hit on people with blood oozing out of their eye sockets and lumpy buttocks hanging around their ankles.

Apart from attracting hormonally invigorated young men, buttocks have other functions, such as providing soft protection for hips, but most importantly, they're very good for sitting on. Buttocks are not known for being prone to any illnesses, breakages or diseases and are therefore one of the few well designed parts of the human anatomy. At least for those happy enough with the size they were allocated.

One downside of a nice butt, is that when attached to young boys, buttocks become very attractive to priests and old school masters who liked to bend young lads over and beat them in order to satisfy some of their urges. Thankfully this sort of thing has been curtailed in most civilized societies.

Buttocks - 9/10

LEGS

Legs generally do their job fairly well. It's only when you try to do things like going up or down stairs, or running, or turning quickly, that they can be troublesome.

Over eighty percent of professional athletes sprain their ankles more than once. Other types of leg injury are also common. You can pull a hammy, tear a ligament, rupture an Achilles, turn an ankle, break an ankle, fracture a tibia, break a fibula, snap a femur, or toss a paella.

Another issue for sporty types is athlete's foot, also known as stinky jock sock or smelly sock syndrome, which is a very common problem for teenage boys, whether they're good at running or not. It's an even bigger problem for anyone in the vicinity of a teenage boy when he takes his shoes off.

If you want to be a professional athlete but don't want to risk leg injuries, you can have your lower legs removed and replaced with blades of springy carbon fiber. This will allow you to run fast in complete safety, both in training and in competition. It will also make you immune to athlete's foot.

The downside is that when you're not running, the blades make you walk like an emu and can also have the side-effect of making you shoot your girlfriend through the bathroom door.

Legs have inspired some great works of art, although the titular song that commences with the line, "She's got legs, she knows how to use them" is not considered to be amongst them.

According to myth and legend Achilles was hit in the heel with a poisoned arrow. New research indicates that something quite different occurred. An ancient scroll, recently discovered by Tom Hanks in a tomb beneath the Vatican, reveals that Achilles' Achilles' heel was actually his inability to run, or even walk quickly, due to a birth defect. Whilst laboriously trudging his way to battle, he was bitten in the heel by a snapping turtle. Achilles' fans changed the story because it was so embarrassing for their hero to get his comeuppance in such a way. To make the lie more convincing, they made up the whole backstory about him being dunked in the Styx as a baby. Achilles' demise is in fact the true origin of the term "snapping at your heels."

Good work Tom Hanks. Or as his close friends would say, thanks, Tanks.

As a footnote to this story, Achilles was reputed to have killed Hector, then threaded leather thongs through incisions next to Hector's Achilles' tendons and dragged him behind a chariot. Had the turtle snapped Achille's Achille's tendon a little earlier, it might have been named the Hector's Protector turtle rather than the more mundane snapping turtle.

A common affliction of the upper inner thigh is chafing, which is mostly suffered by long distance athletes, sweaty fat buggers out for a gentle stroll or girls with boyfriends too lazy to shave.

Legs - 6/10

KNEES

Knees are a problem. Mainly because they're just not strong enough for the job. Any kind of load or stress can injure them. Fear can make them tremble, as can upright coitus. Ligaments and cartilage are easily torn. Knees can fracture, swell and freeze. And when they get a bit of age on them they can develop osteoarthritis. They should be built out of a tougher material. Like titanium. Which they probably will be if you have to have them replaced.

Knees are also a problem in that they attract the attention of kneecapping fetishists. Kneecapping fetishists often find employment with criminal or terrorist organisations. Unlike foot fetishists, kneecapping fetishists actually do have a gun in their pocket and thus being the target of one of them is a lot less pleasant than noticing a damp patch developing in the trousers of the shoe sales assistant as he eases your foot into a loafer. Certainly neither event is fun to be part of but at least you get to walk away from one of them.

Knees are often hit by doctors with small hammers, although nobody's quite sure why. It is thought that the practice was first seen in a movie called Doctor Doctor in 1943, which was the story of a single woman who was so keen to have a son who was a doctor that she legally changed her surname to Doctor, and then named her first born son Doctor, just to make sure.

Unfortunately Doctor Doctor didn't manage to qualify for medical school and went to work in a hospital as a janitor. One day there was an emergency, and on hearing someone call doctor, Doctor Doctor looked up and before he could dispel the error, was rushed by the arm to the emergency room.

A dazed looking patient was sitting on the edge of a bed and Doctor Doctor, who happened to be carrying a small hammer, was asked to diagnose the patient's condition.

Doctor Doctor commenced the consultation by giving the patient a light tap on each knee. The reflexive kicks caused the nurses to start giggling which encouraged Doctor Doctor to repeat the action. The ensuing hilarity and applause caused more and more people to gather round and Doctor Doctor was carried away in the moment, performing more and more intricate rhythmic tapping routines on the knees of the unfortunate patient, who subsequently required bilateral knee replacement surgery.

After being dismissed by the hospital, Doctor Doctor began to perform the routine as a side show in a travelling circus, before turning the act into a very lucrative new branch of medicine called Reflexology, thus finally fulfilling his mother's dreams.

Knees - 3/10 (Too fragile, insufficiently flexible.)

FANKLES

A foot without an ankle is as useless as an ankle without a foot. Because feet and ankles always work together as a unit, it makes sense to judge them together. Hence, fankles.

Feet come in three different sizes, small, medium and large, and three different varieties, normal, flat and club. This can cause confusion when trying to order coffee and sandwiches in a podiatrist's office, but fortunately that's not something that happens more than a couple of times every day.

Apart from that, you'd think that feet, as opposed to ankles, wouldn't cause too much trouble. But they have a few problems of their own, including the previously mentioned athlete's foot, bunions, onions, ingrown toenails, fungal infections, mushroom bloom, Morton's neuroma, plantar fasciitis, plantar warts and stress fractures.

If you've ever made the mistake of talking to an assistant in a sports shoe outlet, you'll probably have been put through a tedious routine involving pronation, overpronation, underpronation, mispronunciation, goose gait, marble arch and heel strike. The likelihood of walking out of the shop with a pair of shoes that fits isn't increased by enduring this humiliation. It should be avoided if at all possible.

It has been suggested that sales techniques of this variety were actually invented by Jeff Bezos in order to encourage the move to online shopping.

Other forms of foot fetishism include sniffing, licking and ritual foot washing. When men give foot washings to other men in a public place or place of worship it is customary for the foot washer to wear loose flowing robes to conceal evidence of arousal.

There is a particular breed of fish that has a human foot fetish, in that they like to nibble at hardened and loose skin. It's advisable to consult a reliable reference book to identify the fish variety before dipping your feet into a new pond, as some South American fish bite off more than just the loose skin. Not recommended in the open ocean.

The foot isn't a terrible piece of design, but like most other parts, it's very easy to come up with a better one.

Toenails serve no function at all. Fingernails, can be useful, especially for boy scouts and others who need to undo tight knots, but toenails are a maintenance nuisance at best and another source of pain at worst.

What's the point of individual toes? Surely it would be better if the toes were webbed, or enclosed in a single slab of meat. They'd be less likely to be injured, and less likely to stink or develop flakey skin. The only upside of individual toes with toenails, like so much of the poorly designed human body, is that they are job creators. In this case for podiatrists. And vendors of ineffective toenail fungus cures.

Perhaps hooves would've been better than soft skinned soles. If you've ever tried a bare-footed walk for any distance on rough surfaces, you'll wonder how feet could have possibly been designed with soft soles. Just like many other body parts, feet have forced mankind to design workarounds, aka body hacks, aka add-ons, to compensate for not very intelligent design. Along with corrective lenses, sun glasses, sun screen, hats, and underpants, some form of foot protection is almost always a necessity.

Only when lounging around the house, or on the beach in warm climes, are bare feet the most comfortable option. Without warm, protective footwear, living in most parts of the world would be unbearable.

A long time ago many Chinese people believed they could enhance the visual proportions and desirability of their daughters, not by increasing the size of their buttocks, but by decreasing the size of their feet. They tried to improve on the original design by tightly binding the feet of young girls to prevent normal growth. Thankfully that incredibly cruel

NOT VERY INTELLIGENT DESIGN

tradition is now dead and gone, with the last cases reported in the late 1950s.

Unfortunately, many millions of people today still follow a woefully misguided belief that they can improve on the original design by violently mutilating the genitalia of young girls. Education and enlightenment will also, hopefully soon, rid the world of this vile, primitive depravity.

Feet are often susceptible to being tickled. Why ticklishness was included as a design feature of the feet, or anywhere else for that matter, is a mystery, as it seems to serve no purpose at all. And why it makes people laugh when it's neither funny nor particularly enjoyable, is also a mystery. Although some people do seem to get some form of sexual gratification from it. There's even a thing called "competitive endurance tickling" apparently, although whether it was ever really a thing or just one pervert's nasty and expensive hobby is difficult to ascertain.

Ankles work fairly well, but do injure much too easily. Should be more robust.

Fankles - 2/10 (Without protection they're an ouch with every footstep.)

INFANCY

Human infants are the most incompetent and incontinent of any creature on planet earth. They require years of constant attention just to keep them alive. You can house train four generations of cats in the time it takes one human child to figure out how to stop shitting and pissing all over itself. When the wee one eventually discovers self-powered mobility, parents face years of being on almost constant suicide watch as the slow learning infant devises ways to cut, bruise, fall, drown, stab, electrocute and pour boiling water on itself. And that's just inside the house.

Baby giraffes drop 6 feet from their mom's vagina, slam onto the ground, and within an hour they're walking around. So the baby steps video of a 10-month-old human is really not impressive. Baby birds leap out of the nest and fly two weeks after hatching. By the time baby humans begin to crawl, birds are having their own babies. Exactly when, if, or how they learn to avoid shitting in their own nests is not well documented.

We may end up being smarter than sparrows, but out of the blocks we're very slow learners, especially of the basics, such as eating, shitting, walking, crawling, staying alive, staying alive.

Eating, shitting, walking, crawling, staying aliiiiiiiiive.

Infancy - 5/10 (Because for all their nuisance value, babies are still very cute.)

DOTAGE

The designer did a really, really poor job of organizing how human life should end. If you've lived a sensible life, haven't pumped too many recreational poisons through your system, and are lucky enough to have avoided major health issues along the way, you're still reasonably likely to die a drawn out, painful death.

Barring accidents, the effects of old age are likely to begin decades before your ultimate demise. The ageing process disables you slowly, bit by bit, an ache here, a pain there, a malfunction somewhere else, gradually enfeebling your body, and often your mind, until you eventually need to be cared for like an infant. Albeit a sick old one who gets progressively more helpless. And then you die.

If you're not one of the healthy ones, there's a good chance you'll live for an uncomfortable number of years with varying degrees of pain and discomfort courtesy of one or more age-related diseases such as atherosclerosis, cardiovascular disease, cancer, arthritis, cataracts, osteoporosis, diabetes, hypertension or Alzheimer's disease.

A tiny minority are lucky enough to die in their sleep without too much pain in the final few weeks. For those that aren't so lucky, it may be advisable, as in so many health related areas, to take matters out of the designer's hands, if at all possible. Anyone who's had the misfortune to watch their parents die of old age, knows that natural death is a design feature that often involves terrible suffering.

A brain that could automatically produce its own anesthetic chemicals to counter ageing related illnesses and make the twilight days slide into a pleasant morphine or opium-like state of consciousness, but with sufficient clarity to relate to and communicate with loved ones would be a design feature that would greatly enhance the dying process.

Ageing and Death by Natural Causes - 0/10

PHYSICAL PERFORMANCE

Running and Jumping

Any half decent designer would have given us the ability to run like Steve Austin, the Six Million Dollar Man. Steve had the ability to take huge strides, often seemingly in slow motion, whilst covering massive distances faster than a speeding car. When he got up a serious head of steam, Steve made a noise something like someone gently shaking a length of tinfoil or aluminum wrap in a moderate breeze. It was unclear if the noise came from his legs or his ass. Either way, it was cool.

Humans should be easily the fastest runners on the planet. And the best jumpers. And the best tree climbers. And the strongest. Why not? Given the opportunity to design the greatest creature on the planet, why design something relatively slow and weak?

Even when they don't jump the start, Cheetahs can easily beat us in a running race over any distance. Some people say they're only good over a short distance but that's not true. If they get tired they just lie down, wait for the human to catch up, eat the human, and they're good to go again.

But it's not only cheetahs. There are any number of animals that can run faster than us. It's why we invented guns. There used to be a rule that you were only allowed to shoot as much as you could eat that day. The rule was eased when we started shooting each other, and it was all but lost from the collective memory by the time we invented the machine gun. At one time, army generals believed that battles could be won if enough foot soldiers ran towards enemy machine guns. It is not officially recorded exactly how many generals personally ran towards enemy machine guns, but the broad consensus is that the number is extremely close to zero.

Running - 2/10

Climbing

We're not as good as the average goat when it comes to climbing. And nowhere near as good as the average mountain goat. Which seems ridiculous when you look at them. The cloven hoof would appear to be vastly inferior to the human hand for climbing purposes. And it's not only the mountain variety of goat that can scale things. There are many photographs of spindly trees packed with goats standing around on skinny branches, right up to the top, calmly snacking on the few remaining leaves. They generally remain in the tree until they've achieved complete defoliation.

A mountain goat is reputed to have been the first creature to climb to the top of Mt Everest back in the 16th century, a time when foliage was fairly widespread throughout the Himalayas. The goat reputedly ate the two small bushes at the summit, then finished off every remaining piece of shrubbery during a leisurely descent. This is why the summit is bare today and also why there's no longer any oxygen up there. (Bovine flatulence is commonly blamed for making a large contribution to climate change, but when you consider what goats did to the Himalayan flora, and the fact that they're also prolific farters, an argument could be made that cows have been unfairly maligned on this subject.) Goats are either complete idiots when it comes to conservation, or they have the same cavalier disregard for the longevity of the planet as energy company executives and their beholden political lackeys. But they do taste good in curry.

Though goats are better than humans at climbing, they're not a patch on monkeys. Those hairy little buggers can run up trees. Fast. They could probably run up Everest too, if there were any bananas left up there to make it worth their while. They can turn a huge palm tree into a fairground attraction, flying around the outside like they're on a swing chair carousel. They don't look all that different from us, but in this department their physical superiority is an embarrassment to all humans. They're not widely known as tasting good in curry.

Climbing - 3/10 (Including a bonus point for a human being second to the top of Everest.)

Swimming

We can learn to swim, to a certain extent, but even the best swimmers on earth are comically inept compared to many other creatures. Imagine lining up at the Olympic swimming finals and someone slips a small dolphin into lane eight. Oh the humiliation. Or if, when the starting gun sounds, a cormorant flies into the venue, dives into the pool, laps the field then takes off and flies out again. Fifteen years of getting out of bed every morning before dawn, only to end up looking ponderously slow and stupid.

It'd be like a class of fifth year guitar students if Jimi Hendrix walked in, shredded it for five minutes before smashing the guitar to bits, setting it on fire and walking out. The kids would look at each other, put down their guitars and leave, never to touch one again. No point.

But back to the cormorant. Those little buggers can fly, as well as swim way better than us. They sit on the edge of the jetty looking at humans like we're so inferior we hardly warrant their attention. If we get too close they casually move away. They can walk, but rarely do, as walking's the least effective way they have of getting anywhere. Generally, they'll fly to wherever they want to go, be it a beach, a tree, a cliff top, or they may choose to land on water. Where, if they get hungry, they'll submerge and swim better than the fish below, which they eat fresher than the freshest sashimi anybody's ever tasted, before relaxing, stretching their wings as they dry off in the sun. No wonder they look at us with such disdain. In certain parts the cormorant is commonly known as the shag, and they're probably good at that too.

Free diving is an activity in which idiots risk their lives to see if they can stay underwater for about a hundredth of the time a whale can. It's as pointless as mountain climbing, and potentially as risky, as your blood might boil or your lungs might collapse, but at least your fingers and nose don't turn black and fall off.

Swimming - 1/10 (Better than drowning.)

General Fitness

For humans to attain and maintain a decent level of physical performance, exercise is required. At least for adults.

Lions and jaguars sleep through most of every day, without ever dreaming of doing a press up, a chin up, or going for a light jog. (This is one of those things that requires no scientific study. You just know it's true. No amount of scientific study will ever establish what big cats do in fact dream of.)

Without a hint of a warm up, or a stretch, they're off, out of the blocks like a spring-loaded blade-runner, nary a thought of a pulled hammy. They catch lunch, kill lunch, eat lunch, and take the rest of the afternoon off. Not one of them is overweight, and they always look fabulous. Hair just the right length, perfectly groomed, just the right amount of muscularity. Toned like they've been to the gym three times this week. Except they haven't. They never work out at all. Not for one second. They only ever break a sweat if that's exactly what they're in the mood to do. They never give a moment's thought to any crazy diet fads and never pay a few hundred bucks to go to a gym twice in January. No lion has ever taken advantage of the extended payment plan to buy an ab-blasting machine from the home shopping network. They don't need it. They look great and they know it. Whenever they sense a camera they can turn on Blue Steel or Le Tigre faster than Derek Zoolander.

The only time they don't look great is when they're getting really old or when some ugly, ghoul-faced moron is posing with their corpse, having just committed the vile and cowardly act of murdering them. Which, for some hard to comprehend reason, makes certain shit-for-brains assholes feel good about themselves. But enough of deviant scum.

For normal humans the old cliché, no pain, no gain, is true. One of the only times you'll see a large gathering of humans that look as toned as a pride of leopards is at the Olympics.

Actually the correct collective noun for leopards is a leap, but a pride sounds better. A pride works for any fine looking group of individuals, regardless of species. A pride of Olympic athletes. A pride of jaguars. A pride of Ferraris. A pride of F-18s. As far as jaguars go, the accepted collective noun seems to be a prowl, a shadow or a jamboree, which makes them sound like girl scouts. A prowl and a shadow are actually pretty damn good, but a pride's still better, because they're such magnificent animals. A pride of jaguars. The reason that the accepted collective noun for jaguars doesn't readily spring to mind may be that they don't usually hang around in groups. Unlike owners of classic Jaguar automobiles, whose collective noun is a cardigan. A cardigan of classic Jag owners.

Here are a few more examples of appropriate collective nouns. A hairball of hunters. A shithole of shooters. A nightmare of NRA members. A portaloo of pussy-grabbing pissants.

For most normal humans, even trying to look like a healthy specimen involves self-control, hard work and pain. This is a design fault. We should have been designed to look fabulous, and perform brilliantly, without having to devote an hour or two, every single bloody day, to physical exercise.

Why not make ice cream and chocolate and cookies and beer really beneficial to a fine physique? Oooh, my belly's looking a tiny wee bit flabby. Better have a couple more beers followed by a bowl or two of ice cream to metabolize the shit out of that.

Physical performance - 2/10 (Because there are a few animals that are slower and weaker than us. But not many.)

FLYING

Why not? Lots of things do. Birds, insects, bats, foxes, fish, boomerangs.

It took us thousands of years to figure out how to fly and then only with machines. Birds and insects figure out how to fly before they learn how to talk or walk properly.

Wouldn't it be wonderful if we could fly like birds? Rather than substituting arms for wings, like birds, we should have wings in addition to arms. There are plenty of creatures with more than four limbs, ants, spiders and centipedes for example, so as a concept, it's not far-fetched. A bumblebee has six limbs, plus wings. Four limbs, plus wings is not at all unreasonable.

But then again, perhaps we could have rocket style outlets in our fingertips for VTOL capability. When digestion takes place a certain amount of food would be processed into highly compressed rocket fuel which could be expelled from our fingertips at will. This would be a huge improvement. It's probably worth pointing out here that the great designer also designed volcanoes, so a form of rocket thrust is, in principle, part of his established repertoire. Plus of course, he can theoretically make up the rules as he goes along.

Given all of the above, what sort of idiot (or miserable bastard?) would set out to design the greatest creature on earth and decide to exclude the ability to fly? Most people would love to be able to fly.

It's been suggested that ingesting certain drugs, LSD for example, can make people believe they can fly, causing them to jump from high places and accidentally die. The most commonly cited example of this was during the CIA's MKUltra experiments in the 1950s. A recent investigative documentary makes the more plausible case that the man was in fact thrown out the window because the CIA concluded that he'd become a liability to the program.

Tales of astral planing and levitation are further evidence that mankind would really love to be able to fly. Videos of cross-legged people bouncing across the floor are evidence that some people are delusional. Snapping awake at the end of a falling dream is about as real as unassisted human flying gets. At least for people who are regarded as being sane.

Wing suits don't count as they are yet another example of a human designer stepping in to make up for a deficiency in the original design.

Flying - 0/10 (Deserves minus 10.)

ART AND MUSIC

The greatest scientific and industrial achievements are often regarded as the most significant accomplishments of humanity. But as brilliant as jumbo jets, sky scrapers, iPads and penicillin are, a big part of what separates man from other animals is artistic talent. The ability to imagine and create works that inspire, enthrall and entertain others.

The sensation of being emotionally moved by a great piece of music, whether performed by a symphony orchestra, a solo voice or a three-piece rock band, is like magic. If you emerge from a movie theatre, blinking and needing a moment to remember who and where you are, having being totally absorbed in another world for two hours, then you've just experienced a great piece of human artistic endeavor. Similarly, great works of poetry, literature, dance, architecture and the visual arts have the potential to elevate the spirit of most humans in a way that seems to be beyond most animals.

Which is almost worth a perfect score. But, whereas the majority of people have the ability to appreciate and be moved by some form of art, far fewer have the talent to create things truly worthy of admiration. In most endeavors, that doesn't really matter. There are enough talented painters, writers, designers, song writers and poets to fill the world with wonderful things. People who aren't good at those things sometimes have a bit of a dabble before giving up and leaving it to those who are.

But. Big but. Lots of us can't sing in tune. There's no good reason to design humans that way. The sound of people singing out of tune is truly awful and totally unnecessary. Whether they're at a karaoke bar or standing next to you at a concert, there's no quicker way for a stranger to attract a death wish than to sing out of tune in someone else's ear.

There could still be truly outstanding, unique voices like Pavarotti, Sinatra, Willie Nelson, k d lang and many more, but what if every single person in a football stadium could really hold a tune. Imagine that.

Art and Music - 8/10

PAIN AND INJURY

There's a good reason for pain to be a feature of the human body. For example, it'd be really annoying to spend a minute or two leaning on a barbecue before noticing your hand was medium rare.

But does pain really have to be quite so intense? If the maximum level of pain were akin to a sharp slap on the wrist, surely that'd be enough to sound the alarm and make us take action to prevent further harm.

Likewise, if the psychological pain associated with such things as humiliation, betrayal, hangovers, grief and lost love were not quite so severe, life would be more pleasant. Or at least not quite so occasionally brutal.

Decreased pain levels would also make torture much less attractive to sadists, dictators, vice presidents and secretaries of defense.

One brilliant design feature is the ability to heal. A small cut can heal itself completely within just a few days. Larger injuries may require a bit of attention to stop the blood flow or to hold the injured bits together, but they too will heal. Serious injuries may require serious medical intervention, but once again, provided the damage isn't too extreme, our bodies will eventually heal and we'll be good to go again.

Healing - 8/10 (Points off for limb regrowth and spinal cord recovery.)

Pain - 5/10 (Sound idea, over-zealous execution.)

DISEASES

When you've had the good fortune of living for a few years with uninterrupted good health, it comes as a bit of a shock to suddenly find yourself feeling sick. Often for absolutely no reason that you can think of. It could be any one of dozens of things. Actually more than dozens of things. For some reason our designer came up with a bewildering number of illnesses that can afflict the human body. A wide ranging spectrum of misery, from small, easily treated, one or two day, barely noticeable irritations, to cancer. Fuck cancer. Who the hell designed that? Some total asshole. The same asshole it would seem, that invented flesh-eating bacteria. Along with a whole lot of other naturally occurring atrocities.

In the early days of ocean exploration, whole crews would fall sick, and, if they remained at sea for a few months, they'd all die. It takes about six weeks for scurvy to set in and the results are horrifying. Wounds that don't heal, spontaneous bruising, rotting gums, personality changes, bleeding, madness, infection and, when death finally comes, it's a mercy. It took people a fair while to figure out why everybody got scurvy on sea journeys. The answer was in their diet. Scurvy develops in the human body as a result of insufficient vitamin C. We now know how important fruit and veg are in a balanced diet, but we didn't understand it back then.

And here's the kicker. Almost all animals synthesize their own vitamin C, but humans don't. Huge design fault. Dogs would have been fine going on long ocean journeys, had they invented sailing ships, but silly old humans set out on boats before they'd discovered some very important things about their dietary requirements. And before they'd invented refrigeration.

There are plenty of diseases that affect some animals but not humans, and plenty of diseases that affect some humans but not others. Highly intelligent human scientists have studied many of theses diseases and found out how to make all humans immune to some of the nastier ones. Far less intelligent humans have subsequently decided to not only make their children take their chances with these deadly diseases, but to put everybody else at risk too.

There's an old joke that goes a little bit like the following. An Englishman a Welshman and an anti-vaxxer are the last survivors on an island afflicted with a terrible contagious disease. The survivors are all carriers of the disease, but not sufferers. They find a magic lamp. The genie gives them three wishes. One each. The Englishman and the Welshman both wish to be transported back home immediately, and to arrive disease free. Poof, and they're gone. The anti-vaxxer looks around and says, "It's going to get lonely around here." The genie says, "I know this one. You wish your friends were back here with you." "No," says the anti-vaxxer, I want to go home too." "Righto. Disease free like the others?" says the genie. "No, thanks. I don't believe in that vaccine nonsense. Just send me back as I am."

Diseases aren't a challenge, they're just horrible, and suffering isn't good for the human soul, regardless of what some deluded saints may say. Humans don't need physical suffering to make life challenging. We just need each other for that.

Of the 15 leading causes of death in the United States, all of them are down to disease-related design faults except for accidents, in at number 4, and suicide at number 10. And most of them are really, really, seriously horrible, painful ways to die. And that's just the bad ones. The world would be a far better place without even the milder, easily survivable diseases and illnesses, such as the common cold. And we could definitely do without a flu season every bloody year.

A much better way to have designed the human body would be to have made it with an immune system that works better. However it works, whatever it does, turn it up. Turn it up to 12 if necessary.

Disease susceptibility - 0/10 (Total design fail.)

VENEREAL DISEASE

VD. WTF?

Except we don't call it VD any more. To be more up to date, the World Health Organization has recommended STI as the "preferred term" since 1999. What? Changing the fucking name does not help.

VD, STD, STI. Call them what you will, they are an abomination. What sort of perverse psychopath could dream up such things?

The act of male/female copulation is an absolute requirement (at least it used to be) for the human species to survive, yet some complete asshole designed and released a range of diseases to be transmitted, primarily, by taking part in the procreation procedure. Unbelievable.

The ASHA reports that, "more than half of all people will have an STD/STI at some point in their lifetime". More than half of all people will have an STD/STI at some point in their lifetime. Deliberate repetition. Seriously. Who designed that shit?

For a long time, syphilis and gonorrhea were death sentences. Until science intervened with the discovery of penicillin. And then along came AIDS and Herpes. Brilliant!

And the icing on the stupid cake is the fact that the most effective way of preventing the transmission of STIs also guarantees the extinction of the species.

All of which has to make STDs a strong contender for whatever is the absolute opposite of an intelligent design award.

STDs - 0/10 (Only a psychopath would design such things.)

BEHAVIOR

The fact that we need a word for genocide is a big black mark in the human behavior department.

But there are many similar words such as annihilation, carnage, extermination, elimination, liquidation, eradication, decimation, mass murder, massacre, slaughter, final solution, butchery, blood letting, pogrom, ethnic cleansing and holocaust. Which in itself is damning evidence regarding the state of the human condition.

Tragically there are a lot more words meaning similar things (one website lists 158 synonyms for genocide) and for each one of those words there are many examples of the horror that they describe actually occurring. We can be a truly awful pack of bastards, and we often are.

Even if most of us aren't genocidal maniacs or psychopaths, we are a very violent species. Some recent research said that across all mammal species, animals had a 1 in 300 chance of being killed by one of their own. For humans a few thousand years back it was 1 in 50. We're naturally bad, angry, violent bastards. Only in the last few hundred years, have we established a few societies with cultures that reject violence and have functional legal systems and law enforcement. This drops the man on man killing rate down to 1 in 10,000. So it seems possible that we can use our intellect to overcome our violent base instincts, which is promising, but the amount of war and violence that still goes on is nothing to be proud of.

In addition to being violent, it's not uncommon for people to lie, to cheat, to steal, to bully, to commit sex crimes, to be bigots, to take risks that endanger others and to be greedy. These all seem to be naturally occurring instincts that go totally against The Golden Rule, which is the simple moral code that would benefit everybody if it was universally observed - Behave towards others as you would like them to behave towards you.

If only people would behave. But we don't.

A better designed human mind would have the empathy knob turned up. Way up. It is theoretically possible for humans to establish societies where most, if not all, of the inhabitants have a reasonable chance at living a decent life. Unfortunately the great majority of our societies or "cultures" are nothing like this.

Not very long ago we used to have a few ideologically advanced societies that genuinely stood for justice, freedom, democracy and equal human rights. But the rich and powerful are not inclined to settle for enough. They continually try to find ways to make themselves richer and more powerful. Like terminators. They never stop. It's what they do. And for the ultra rich and powerful to attain ultimate levels of wealth and power, the masses must become their opposite. Ultimate wealth and power involves the control of governments, initially through lobbying and bribery to establish favorable legislation, and finally by coup, whether subtle or brazen.

All that is required for a socially responsible democracy to die, is for good people to stop fighting hard to protect it.

We often refer to wealth and power as though they were two separate things. Mostly they're not. It would require an unusual situation or turn of events for a rich person to feel powerless. Or for a powerful person to remain poor. An impoverished union organizer doesn't generally stay that way if he rises to the top.

Another way to attain and wield power, if you're not rich, is to have some sort of cult or fanatical following. Which, once again, often leads to riches. And brainwashed sex partners. And pedophilia. Do pedophiles become preachers, or do preachers become pedophiles? Why there's such a preponderance of sexual deviance amongst those who preach needs to be researched. And the problem eradicated. There are things that should never be tolerated.

A few of humanity's less honorable traits can, however, occasionally be justified. Not bullying. Or pedophilia. Or genocide. Or bigotry. But there is a form of discrimination that's not quite bigotry that can sometimes be justified. If the focus of your discrimination happens to be a group of genocidal maniacs hell bent on your destruction, tolerance of them may well be suicidal. In other words, those who tolerate the intolerance of others, eventually fall victim to that intolerance.

Most humans behave reasonably well most of the time, but a large number don't behave very well at all. And those that behave really badly make life miserable for many others. In other words, the designer didn't establish a decent balance of good, who gives a crap, and evil. Not that everyone should be really happy, all the time, living in a shiny magical kingdom. That would be boring beyond belief. But life poses enough challenges for most people without needing any genocide, or war, or slavery, or oppression, or any of that really bad shit.

Behavior - 0/10 to 10/10

DRUGS

This is following on from the behavior section, which means it's about recreational or psychotropic drugs, rather than medicinal or curative ones.

Humans love getting high. Out to lunch, off our faces, out of our heads, sloshed, smashed and hammered. Birds, elephants, monkeys, reindeer, opossums, jaguars, gorillas and many other animals all love getting shitfaced too. If you don't understand why, there are a few substances you should probably have a bit of a go at. Just for educational purposes.

There's an old saying that goes, "everything in moderation". Oscar Wilde and/or Benjamin Franklin reputedly pointed out that everything in moderation included moderation, but neither of them stressed the point that everything includes everything. So it's probably not great advice.

Drugs can be fun. Also the opposite. They can start off as fun and move on to utterly destroying people's lives and ultimately killing them.

Even the world's favorite drug, alcohol, is very far from perfect. If you drink enough to have an outstandingly good time, you'll suffer all the next day. And it turns some people into complete dickheads. Or at least reveals the dickhead that's normally restrained within.

Assuming the designer that designed humans also designed naturally occurring recreational drugs, and how we react to them, how about a drug that makes everybody happy and witty and feel fantastic mentally and physically and that you can't overdose on, yet it still allows you to drive safely and has no hangover attached to it? Why didn't the great designer design one of those, instead of the huge variety of drugs that have one or two upsides but a great many more downsides?

Perfect recreational drugs are easy to imagine, but for some reason none have been designed. Yet.

Recreational drugs - 0/10 to 8/10

INTELLIGENCE

Below average intelligence. To utter those words in public is to risk being chastised by any social justice warrior who happens to be within earshot. But half the population does have a level of intelligence that falls below the median, regardless of how you define intelligence. It's merely stating the obvious. An indisputable fact. At least among those who don't need to redefine words in order to try to explain their woolly thinking.

It's said that if you don't know who the mark is at a poker table, you're it. It's the same thing for intelligence. If you can't tell who the stupidest person in the room is, you're probably it.

But that doesn't take into account the Dunning-Kruger effect. Which explains why the stupidest person may believe that they're actually the smartest. The reason for this is that really stupid people have such limited knowledge that they have absolutely no idea how much they don't know. Which can cause them to think that perhaps they know a fair bit about something when in fact they know very little.

People who score 95 percent or more in exams, usually estimate their result will be two or three percentage points below their actual score. Because they know exactly what they got right and don't give themselves the benefit of the doubt on things that they may have got right by luck or guesswork. People who score 75 to 90 percent generally estimate they'll get pretty close to what they in fact score. They'll know what they got right, and add a few points for things they may or may not have guessed correctly. People who score 50 or less usually overestimate their result, sometimes by a lot, because they'll give themselves credit for all their answers, even though a lot of them will be wrong.

Einstein, or somebody else, said that one of the effects of a great amount of learning was that it made one aware of how much one still didn't know. Which is not a realization that occurs to the brutally ignorant. As Bertrand Russell said, "One of the painful things about our time is that those who feel certainty are stupid, and those with any imagination and understanding are filled with doubt and indecision."

If you've spent any time in conversation with stupid people, you'll realize that the designer of mankind once again failed in terms of dishing out a reasonable amount of smarts to a reasonable amount of people.

Thankfully the highly intelligent minority have contributed disproportionately to the advancement of humankind and civilization, and with the collective pooling of knowledge since the invention of the printing press, that advancement is likely to proceed at an ever increasing pace.

But. There are some potential handbrakes to our continuing advancement, notably social media, which serves to amplify the opinions of stupid people who previously had no way to access mass communication, nuclear war, and/or the ascendancy of groups of people of faith who regard science and human rights as blasphemy.

Intelligence - 0/10 to 9/10 (It varies. The 10 is reserved because the most intelligent people are probably yet to be born.)

MENTAL HEALTH

According to the World Health Organization, one in four people will be affected by some form of mental disorder at some time in their lives. In other words, twenty-five percent of all human brains roll off the assembly line with inherent problems. By any standards, that's a serious quality control failure.

The problems include depression, bipolar disorder, dementia, schizophrenia, anxiety disorders and lots of other things, all of which can make people's lives thoroughly miserable. And it's not only the afflicted who suffer. The people surrounding them are also adversely affected.

Many books have been written about the difficulties of living with people with personality disorders and other mental conditions. Unfortunately, it's not at all unusual for people with serious sociopathic tendencies to rise to positions of power in both the private and public sectors. A lack of empathy and lack of a sense of humor are big clues to help identify sociopaths. History is loaded with tragedies caused by sociopathic despots.

Millions of people can end up suffering because of one person's mental illness.

Although the actions of despotic leaders are the most obvious cases of widespread harm caused by mental derangement, group insanity can also cause major problems.

Other animals occasionally exhibit group insanity, such as pods of whales beaching themselves, or herds of lemmings hurling themselves off cliffs, but humans also exhibit group insanity on a regular basis. Such as believing stories about lemmings hurling themselves off cliffs. Or chemtrails. Or homeopathy. Or a flat earth. Or the concept that uninformed opinions are just as valid as scientifically established facts. Even if they're merely the mindfart of some idiot making shit up, stupid people believe things like the anti-vaccination position, and bleach as medicine, represent the other side of the argument, and deserve consideration.

Humans at various times have conducted, and believed in, many forms of witch hunt, both literal and metaphorical. The specter of satanic ritual abuse has thrown humans into mass hysteria, in some cases resulting in perfectly innocent childcare workers, and others, being locked up and having their lives ruined. Joe McCarthy made himself famous by convincing large numbers of Americans that they had reds under their beds. For this to have taken hold the way it did required the widespread belief that anyone who was of the Communist persuasion was a serious danger to the good ole USA and should be locked up. After it all blew over, people came to their senses and realized that allowing citizens to have differing political views was in fact the essence of democracy rather than its enemy. A point of view which is regularly challenged to this day.

Group insanity is also exhibited by millions of voters who go to the polls and cast ballots in favor of politicians who have no intention of doing anything at all to benefit them. Why ageing wealthy bigots with a history of widening the gap between rich and poor are repeatedly re-elected by an impoverished electorate is a mystery to many. Gerrymandering, voter suppression, gullibility, election tampering and common stupidity are all contributing factors.

Back in the seventies or thereabouts, many people were convinced that rock music played backwards revealed evil messages that would poison young minds and lead to the downfall of decent civilization. Fortunately CDs were more difficult to play backwards than vinyl so this particular piece of group madness was swept away by the advancement of technology.

The resurgence of vinyl may not seem as though it should be part of the mental illness section, but is it any less crazy than a nostalgic resurgence of hand-crafted artisanal beer? Or bicycles with no gears or brakes? How about hand-cranked car windows? Of course vinyl on a decent stereo is far better than having to listen to a song via someone's crackly fucking cellphone speaker, but if you're going to play the vinyl game, why not go reel to reel? The sort of thing you'd buy at an Inconvenience Store. Every old-fashioned, time-consuming, poorly-designed device in one place, way out in the country, right down the end of a rutted, dusty road. That only takes cash and has no change.

The propensity for people to gullibly believe in quackery and snake oil of all sorts is so common that it would take far too much space even to list category titles. For the astrologically minded, here's your horoscope. The positions of the moon and stars will make no difference at all to your life this month. For next month, read that again. Repeat as often as necessary.

Human exuberance for irrationality extends to all sorts of woo woo that can only possibly be as effective as a placebo, because faith-based alternative medical cures and the celebrity vaccine-free lifestyles of the rich and brainless contain nothing else. Which means there may well be a demand for a Homeopathic Cocktail Bar next to the Inconvenience Store. One great feature would be that there's no chance of getting a hangover after a big night at the HCB, even if you down thirty to fifty non-standard drinks. The downside is that there's much less chance of getting laid, on account of the absence of beer or wine goggles.

While the style of thinking that eschews scientific medicine may not be generally thought of as mental illness, it can lead to all manner of actual physical illnesses. Stories about children dying from lack of medical care because of their parents firmly held religious beliefs are way too common.

The reason there's so much on gullibility in the mental health section, rather than the intelligence section, is that intelligent people can often be just as gullible as stupid people. In fact, there's a whole branch of the snake oil industry, uncommonly known as the world of woo woo , as practiced by people such as Deepak Chopra, that's deliberately tailored for the somewhat literate end of society.

Mental Health - 3/10

MEMORY

Poor memory is traditionally associated with old age, but in fact human memory is a lot worse than most people think it is, regardless of how old we are. Most adults have no recall whatsoever of the first four or five years of their lives, and those who think they do are deceiving themselves. Or lying. In other words, when our brains are at their freshest they retain nothing.

Scientific research on human memory indicates that it's a lot less accurate than previously thought, to the extent that legal experts are now beginning to agree that eye witness testimony is not very reliable at all, even when people are doing their best to tell the truth. Ask any two people who were involved in an event a year or two ago, and you'll usually hear two different accounts.

Elephants are reputed to have the best memory of all animals, but no elephant has ever been called as a witness in a murder trial, so whether or not there's any truth in that doesn't really matter.

Eli "Elephant Man" Manson, was a successful sideshow artist, not on account of having a brutally ugly visage, although he was far from an attractive man, but on account of his prodigious memory. Eli could memorize hundreds of words drawn from an audience and regurgitate them without fail. Although this feat delighted most, some punters felt betrayed when he arrived on stage, as they were hoping to see a revolting freak of nature. Occasionally this led to altercations, but despite Eli's protests to management, they insisted on retaining ambiguous promotional material as it worked so well, and most of the disgruntled punters were eventually satisfied by the Elephant Man's performance. Manson's misgivings were ultimately proven correct when a heavily intoxicated man in the front row at a show in rural Georgia, an open carry state, shot him dead for "not being ugly enough".

Eli "Elephant Man" Manson was buried in the Showmen's Rest, which occupies a corner of the Woodlawn Cemetery in Tampa, Florida. He lies there along with many carnival legends including the Human Cannonball, Edmondo "Papa" Zucchini, renowned show owner and sideshow barker, Carl J Sedlmayer, and the Lobster Boy, Grady Stiles.

Grady Stiles was born into the fourth or sixth generation (the historical record, aka the human collective memory, is inconsistent on this) of ectrodactyly afflicted members of the Stiles family who were part of a travelling carnival by reason of their freakishly lobster-like hands and feet. Stiles continued to be known as Lobster Boy into adulthood, where, despite his appearance he was married three times, to two women, and became an abusive alcoholic. In 1978 he shot and killed his daughter's husband-to-be on the eve of their wedding, and was sentenced to fifteen years' probation as the state of Florida could not provide appropriate facilities in which to incarcerate him. His probation included a community service component cleaning toilets at the local Crab Shack.

In 1992 Lobster Boy died after three bullets entered the back of his head as he watched television in his trailer in Gibsonton, or Gibtown, as the locals call it, on Highway 41, just a few miles south of the Showmen's Rest in Tampa. Gibsonton was a popular winter residence and retirement town for carnies, clowns and barkers, and was once known as the strangest town in America. Lobster Boy's wife, in cahoots with her son from a previous marriage (or her son-in-law, depending on which piece of historical memory you read), hired another sideshow artist to perform the hit. The other sideshow artist may have also been her son-in-law. Perhaps the same one, perhaps another. The communal historical memory is unclear on this.

Blockchain technology will help address the problem of the accuracy of the macro-collective memory, but it will do nothing to help individual human memory which seems likely to remain poor until such time as we succeed in integrating artificial memory chips into our neural circuits.

As anyone who's experienced a loved one slowly disappear through the scourge of Alzheimers can tell you, when memory recedes, so does the person you knew. Not just their recall, their whole personality disappears. Without memories we cease to really exist at all. Knowing that memory loss afflicts so many people, you'd think the designer might have worked a bit harder on making human memory a bit more accurate and a lot more durable.

Memory - 3/10 (Without it, we're nothing.)

LOVE

Love is good. Love is fantastic. Amazing. The most unbelievably brilliant thing a human can feel. Better than sex. Because the best sex involves love (at least for the mentally well balanced). Love is the essence of everything worthwhile.

When love goes wrong it can be the most painful thing imaginable. But that can't really be rated as a design fault. Because peaks can't be peaks unless there are corresponding valleys. Love's a big part of being a human animal, and without it human existence wouldn't be the same thing at all.

Love, or things to do with love, can sometimes cause people to murder and do other terrible things. But that's not love's fault. That's mental illness. Most people deal with the ups and downs of love without maliciousness or violence.

Love can exist in many ways. As well as the romantic version, there's also the love of family, the love of beauty, the love of community, and the love of life and nature. Absence of love is when humanity gets ugly. Love is the thing that makes human existence beautiful.

Love - 10/10

REPRODUCTION

Human pregnancy lasts for nine months. For some animals two or three weeks is enough. And why do human babies have to be so damn big? Why not lay a chicken-sized egg and leave it in the warming drawer for a month or two? Wouldn't that be easier for all concerned? Chickens hardly even seem to notice they've popped one out. Why were humans denied this very much easier option when so many creatures on the planet have it?

Human babies are roughly 1/20 of their mother's weight compared to about 1/900 for giant pandas. That's forty-five times as big! A kangaroo pregnancy takes between three and five weeks, and the resulting joey's about the size of a baked bean. Sure it goes on to spend some months in the mother's pouch (which serves as both bedroom and bathroom and therefore doesn't reward dwelling on), but at least the actual birth itself can be assumed to be literally painless.

When everything goes well, the process of human pregnancy involves far more discomfort and pain than should be necessary. But quite often, everything doesn't go well.

A fertilized egg can implant into the fallopian tube, cervix or ovary rather than the uterus, causing an ectopic pregnancy. In days gone by, ectopic pregnancies invariably resulted in death for both mother and child. Even with the best modern surgical assistance the pregnancy usually has to be aborted to save the life of the mother. A fatal design flaw.

Birthing complications such as breech births are compounded by the position of the birth canal which passes through the pelvis. Sometimes a baby's head is bigger than the pelvic opening of the mother. Yet another fatal design flaw, only alleviated by modern surgery. Once again modern scientific invention has to step in to rectify the shortcomings of the designer.

Birth deformities are unusual, but nevertheless occur often enough to blight the lives of thousands. "Nevertheless" could be thought of as a deformity of the etymological kind, and "alwaysthemore" would appear to be an equally valid, but opposite deformity, although it's not actually a word at all. Notwithstanding the aforesaid, birth deformities are considered highly undesirable, except amongst certain performing artist families involved in the sideshow industry, such as the aforementioned Stiles family (aka Lobster Boy et al) who sustained a multi-generational career by passing on a congenital disorder known as ectrodactyly.

Such an impediment would not normally be conducive to a musical career, but it didn't stop either Korean pianist, Lee

NOT VERY INTELLIGENT DESIGN

Hee-ah, or French guitarist, Lord Lokhraed, of black metal band Nocturnal Depression, from pursuing their passion.

Other congenital disorders can result in "pickled punks", which is the term used by carnival folk for anatomically abnormal human fetuses preserved in jars of formaldehyde. Genuine pickled punks can be distinguished from "bouncers", meaning fake ones made from rubber, for their tendency to bounce less than a dead cat upon hitting the ground. Carnies usually only agree to prove their pickled punks are genuine at the point of a gun. Although one or two drop tests may actually improve the deformity and value of the pickled punk, repeated falls result in pickled mush, which has no display value at all.

Giving birth to a human baby has never been simple, or fun. But it used to be a lot worse. Mortality rates were high. About 1 or 2 percent per birth. Or higher, depending on how far back you go. And the survival rates of successfully born infants was a lot worse. Only in recent decades has it become commonplace for pregnancies to result in a healthy mother and child.

Even following a normal, successful birth, a certain amount of recovery is required, as evidenced by an article in the magazine section of a newspaper in New Zealand entitled, "How to successfully take a shit after giving birth." Without reading a single word of it, the mere fact that it was written is another piece of evidence demonstrating that the human

173

reproductive process would have been very much better designed had an intelligent woman been in charge.

Reproduction 3/10   (At least it works most of the time)

WOMAN

Women, for the most part, are a lot better than men. Softer, less hairy and rough, they smell good, and they're a lot less likely to start punching people after six or seven pints of lager. Supposedly they can also multi-task.

Although this book was written about mankind in general, and most of it applies to women as much as to men, it's somewhat male-centric, on account of being written by men. This section is fairly brief, as an acknowledgement of the fact that men don't know much about women and accordingly should keep their stupid bloody opinions to themselves.

Women's breasts are often excellent. The only improvement would be to make perfect ones more common. Which is really just part of the overall design plan to make everyone of both sexes more attractive, as previously discussed. Not only do men really appreciate nice breasts, they also give women power over men. If you have any doubt about that just ask any woman with a great rack.

Similar things can be said about necks, arms, hands, legs etc. An elegant woman is a marvel of sublime design.

But, there are a few things wrong with the design of woman too. The following observations have been supplied by women, including Sinead Ingman, Shantelle Ingman and Esplaine Ingman, second and third cousins of Neel and Mark. So, sisters, if this part gets your hackles up, it's not completely the fault of the evil patriarchy.

Breasts

For exercising they're a pain. Big tits make running difficult. No Playboy centerfold has ever won an Olympic marathon. Even medium sized ones make the steeplechase and similar pursuits more difficult than they'd otherwise be.

Tight bras are very uncomfortable and they cause bulges over the edges, even if you're not fat.

Nipples can be a nuisance. And a dilemma. Some women tape their nipples down to avoid having men look at them. But then they enjoy having them nibbled and bitten at other times. Sometimes women encourage men to bite harder, then in the morning they wonder what the hell that was about?

Of course, given the previously referred to quality control issues, many women find they're not satisfied with what they've been assigned as original equipment, so they opt for a pair designed by a surgeon, who sometimes does a better job than the original designer. And sometimes not.

Boobs - 2/10 to 10/10

Facial hair

Despite an earlier reference to women doing perfectly well without it, it's actually a huge annoyance for many women who feel the need to not only get rid of it, but to do so in a way that allows them to maintain the appearance that there was never any there in the first place. Thus the first choice of men, shaving, is not a good solution for women. Stubble can be seen as manly, but it sure as hell ain't womanly. So plucking, waxing, exfoliating, cream application and all manner of other things are employed.

On catching a glimpse of her blond moustache in a ray of sunlight, Shantelle told Esplaine - "Oh you must do something about that. I have an excellent piece of equipment for it."

Despite the fact that Conchita Wurst won the Eurovision song contest, a full beard will never look good in a ball gown. And neither will balls.

Facial Hair - 0/10

Pubic hair

This is potentially more annoying for women than for men. (Men's pubes stay dry when they pee for a start.) Although some have a fondness for a big hairy bush, the prevailing opinion in modern western society is to respect the bikini line. Many cultures don't have a public bikini line. There's not much published research available there. Beyond the bikini line there are many options including the light trim, the landing strip, the heart, and the full Brazilian. It's difficult and time consuming to do a good job on oneself in the personal topiary department. A black belt in yoga would help with the flexibility issue, but not many people have that. And you often need two hands to stretch the skin as well as a third hand to operate the grooming device. Not easy. Regardless of which option is chosen, it's a big nuisance that could have been entirely avoided with better design.

Pubic hair - 0/10

Leg hair

A bit like the face, but not as much pressure to pretend there was never any hair there. Nevertheless, stubble doesn't look or feel good on a woman's leg. Even a supermodel, qualified in every other way, would have difficulty finding work with stubbly (or hairy) legs and a rainforest sprouting around the edges of her undies.

Leg hair - 0/10

A Google search for hair removal, gets three billion results. It's a massive business. Which is all the evidence you need to declare body hair a complete design disaster. For women and for men.

Menstruation

Most animal species don't have periods. Why did the designer of humans see the need to burden the human female with this monthly chore, inconvenience, annoyance, pain, and test of sanity? The experience varies, from not such a big deal to a week in hell every single month.

Some quotes from the internet -

"the week leading up to it is like playing Russian roulette with my underwear"

"feeling like death"

"if you accidentally hit my boob while I'm on my period I will attack you like a fucking wild animal"

"Someone hold me and tell me this period isn't actually baby Satan trying to rip through my uterus and kill me"

"I never know when it's gonna come and that's why all my panties are stained"

And once again, it's the poor, especially those in third world countries who suffer most, not only through a lack of access to sanitary products, but also because local customs and ancient patriarchal superstitions often make the physical design flaw a much, much bigger problem, in the way menstruating women are treated. Even in a country like the USA, millions of women, including the poor, the homeless, and those in prison can't afford the products which have been designed to help deal with this awful design blunder.

For some reason the designer thought it was a good idea to foist this thing on the human female when most species on earth have no need for it at all. Beyond stupid. Veering towards evil.

Menstruation - 0/10

Pregnancy

Reproduction has been discussed as it applies to the species, but this section is specifically about the pregnancy experience for mothers. Human gestation takes much longer than for most other creatures on planet earth. And during that very long time there are many side effects, which can vary a great deal between individuals, but are almost all extremely unpleasant, including nausea (morning sickness), back ache, constipation, leg cramps, dizziness and fainting, fluid retention (swollen ankles and hands), hemorrhoids (piles), gas and bloating, frequent urination and fatigue. And many more.

As everything mentioned above is a negative, design improvement would be an easy task.

Pregnancy - 3/10 (Some women say they enjoy it.)

Breast feeding

Most mothers and babies seem to enjoy it, and it's a healthy natural thing to do. Although it can involve painful nipples and fatigue.

Breast feeding - 7/10

Opening Jars

Opening jars is something women often turn to men for. They could easily use one of the many tools designed for the purpose, but they often call a man, as a way of reminding that man that they do occasionally find him useful.

Man as tool - 8/10 (Men like to feel useful.)

Driving and Navigation

Most women don't claim to be great drivers, and they're right. Most men think they're good drivers, but they're not. Reversing with a trailer is a skill that eludes most women. And most men too. But it can be learned.

Unlike reading maps. Most women don't claim to be great navigators. Which doesn't stop a man getting angry at a woman because he just drove up a one-way street the wrong way. Many relationships have been jeopardized, and in some cases even terminated, by what began as a disagreement over how to read a map, or more precisely, which way's up.

The invention of GPS has saved many marriages. GPS was not invented by the designer of humans.

Navigation   - No score, superseded skill.

SUMMARY

There are three inexcusable, massive design flaws in the human animal.

1. The combination of breathing and eating tubes.

2. The combination of the sex organs (including free swinging balls) with the excretory organs.

3. The inefficiency of a digestive system that requires the frequent and messy expulsion of half what we consume as shit, farts and piss.

And bad brains.

Four huge design flaws.

Redesigning the human body to do away with just these issues would result in a vastly improved quality of life for all humans. But it's not just these design disasters that are the problem. Every single part of the human body could be improved with better design.

This book assumed the premise that man was created by an intelligent designer. The aim of this book is to appraise the work of the designer.

As a piece of design, carried out by a designer with every possible resource to make the most amazing creature imaginable, and whose design parameters were virtually limitless, man is a very poor piece of work. Even an average human mind, when put to the task, can easily conceive of an animal that is far superior in every way. Some parts are almost okay, others are diabolically stupid.

Man is a seriously flawed design. So flawed in fact, that if we were an early beta version or prototype, we should be scrapped in favor of a clean sheet redesign.

FINAL GRADE

You do the math is one of the most irritating phrases anyone can ever utter. But, if you do decide to do the math, you'll probably find your results don't agree with the stats given below. Which is of no consequence whatsoever as this is a work of unscientific analysis. It is what it is, is another really irritating phrase, but enough of that because enough is enough.

Combining the marks out of ten for all 67 categories gives an average score of 3.7 out of 10. In the old days, that was a fail. In the days of safe spaces and trigger warnings it's a good effort, and nobody should criticize anything about it.

But when you add the appropriate weighting to each of the categories and recalculate the average it comes out at 1.8 out of 10, which really has to be a fail, unless you think everybody who designs anything should get a prize for trying. Or just being themselves and learning to be proud of it.

Design of The Human Animal - 1.8/10   FAIL

CONCLUSION

On the basis of this unscientific analysis, the conclusion can only be that man is a very good example of not very intelligent design. And that's being generous. If an ordinary human can observe the human body and find many ways to improve every aspect of it, the extended conclusion is that the original designer was a moron.

Actually, it's way worse than that. When you consider how much of human existence is taken up with maintenance and repair, wiping bums, dentistry, manflu, fighting, arguing, optometry, pain, illness, despair, depression, infancy and dotage, the human experience could be so much better. And that's the human experience for the lucky ones. For the vast majority, meaning the poor, and especially the poor living in third world countries, life is an ongoing struggle just to survive. Often against horrible diseases for which mankind has already discovered a cure. And the suffering is made worse in billions of cases by the extreme violence and degradation inflicted upon them by other humans. Not only was the designer really,

really bad at designing what is claimed to be the greatest creature in the universe, he was also a psychotic, evil bastard who created far too many psychotic, evil human bastards in his own image.

(That's not to claim that most people are that way inclined, on the contrary, the great majority of people seem to be fundamentally very decent. The point is that even one evil psycho in a thousand is way too many.)

However, on the other hand, if the creator was not a nitpicking, hands on every single thing, kind of designer, and merely threw a big bag of stardust into infinite space and the human animal finally came about following the long term interaction of those tiny particles, following the formation of galaxies, following the collisions of stars, following billions of years of universal interactions, following a series of naturally occurring events stretching all the way back beyond the very first glimmer of single-cell life on planet earth, and we are therefore a continuing work in progress that our growing consciousness and intelligence is now giving us the opportunity to have a hand in forming future versions of, then that is a truly amazing and awe-inspiring situation.

One that's well worth having a damn good think about. Preferably while staring up at the stars on a warm clear night with a fine glass of wine.

The End

P.S. If for some reason the sheer awesomeness of the stars above makes you think there must be a higher power out there who actually gives a shit about you and your life, or whether your team wins on Saturday, just give yourself a quick punch in the nuts (if you have any), imagine choking on your wine, think about cleaning up a big messy crap, and ask why an omnipotent and allegedly benevolent creator would design birth defects, flesh eating bacteria and child cancer.

Then look up again.

To read more by Neel Ingman, go to

neelingman.com

Thanks for reading.

REVIEWS are the best way to help others find books they'll enjoy.

A review that's brief, just a few words, will let other readers know what you liked about the book, and why they may like it too.

So if you enjoyed this book, please leave a review (or at least a rating) at Amazon.com or anywhere else that you can.

And PLEASE DO IT RIGHT NOW before you forget (you know you will).

If you'd like to be notified of new books by Neel Ingman please sign up to the mailing list at

www.neelingman.com

Cheers, Neel

Made in the USA
Las Vegas, NV
26 December 2022

64117598R00111